CW00554478

LET'S RESET

By Suki Thompson
with Rankin

It's time to reset the workplace

Reset something and you adjust it so that it is ready to work again. In our increasingly fast-changing world, the need to keep resetting ourselves is growing – especially at work.

Successful businesses are fundamentally shifting from a time when process, tech, growth and Earnings Before Interest and Tax (EBIT) at any cost were king, to a culture with purpose, resilience and wellbeing at its heart. A culture where people have become the drivers of sustainable growth and commercial outcomes.

Research by Vitality tells us that the best performing organisations gain over 20 days a year of productive time from their employees. These organisations are characterised by an authentic culture of health and wellbeing, accountable leaders who are role models, a comprehensive and effectively communicated programme of interventions, and mentally and physically healthy employees.

I've been struck by the number of celebrities, sports people and high-profile stars coming forward to talk about mental health. Very few business people are doing the same. This book and my company, both called Let's Reset, want to encourage this openness. I hope it will begin to make a difference to the business conversation and to our work culture.

Over the years, I've been inspired and encouraged by conversations with so many business leaders and experts. I've listened to their personal stories of resilience and wellbeing. Some made me cry, others made me gasp in awe, but I have always seen the individuals in a different light, a better light.

So, to push the reset conversation, we have brought together leaders with challenging mental health issues who have achieved prominent roles, companies brilliantly promoting workplace wellbeing, leading practitioners in the mental health arena, and the future generation entering the workplace.

My wonderful and brilliant friend Rankin, who has an ability to see into the soul of every human being, has worked with me on this project. Our collaboration of breathtaking photography and real-life stories brings to life why there is a need for companies to reset their attitudes to mental health, wellbeing and resilience and the success this can bring. The visuals are remarkable. In a world where social media and fake news are distorting our view of ourselves and seriously impacting mental health, Rankin has taken photos of people that reveal aspects of their true selves. These are far from the typical business bio shots. The first looks at Fear Of Missing Out (FOMO). In business, as in life, for our own self-care we need to stop wanting to be involved in everything and the FOMO shot represents this.

The second is a big emotion, not the usual face we show in our working life, but one that expresses the inner anguish, turmoil, pain and pleasure that we feel in our lives and hide from our colleagues. The third is a face palm, to signify the moment when we say, 'No' or 'Stop, think again, be creative', or, 'Just let me reset'. Reset to feel empowered, for more self-care and to channel creativity.

We've grouped the stories into themes.

First there are poignant stories of leaders who have overcome adversity while rising to high-flying roles, then there are leaders who talk about how they have developed their own resilience and wellbeing and how they support colleagues and staff. Thirdly, and unashamedly as an entrepreneur myself (Let's Reset is the fourth business I've founded), we include a set of entrepreneurs. In the fourth section, the magnificent experts, charities and companies working in the industry to support, measure and promote wellbeing share their own advice and stories. Finally, the future generation. We know that wellbeing and resilience must start with the young. Here they talk about how they are building strategies of their own in education, early business and beyond.

Most of all, Let's Reset is meant to inspire us to think differently about the way we work and be brave enough to bring our whole selves to every conversation. There are top tips on how to build your own resilience and wellbeing and an opportunity to glimpse inside the lives of successful business leaders.

If we all take the time to stop and listen, the workplace can be better, happier, and more effective. At the end of the day, I would like every person, no matter how small a part of this book they read, to leave feeling empowered, strong enough to break the pattern of the social media machine and able to talk openly about the importance of wellbeing and resilience at work.

RANKIN

The idea of looking after ourselves at work shouldn't really need an introduction; it should be part of our daily lives. But, like most things that are good for us, we think we can start tomorrow.

I'm someone who has always spent more time working than doing anything else. Even if I look forward to most of it with the excitement and energy I always have, there are moments, and even days, when I don't. Anyone who owns or runs a business that others depend on knows it can get on top of you.

Only a few weeks ago I did a major reset. I put all my businesses together to re-launch them as one: RANKIN. An 80 plus employee company, designed to do an even better job serving brands and to give our people more opportunities to shine and grow. So it's fitting that, at the same time, we are partnering with Suki to help her launch Let's Reset. A perfect reminder that resilience and wellbeing at work won't happen on its own.

None of us are perfect and while we'll have good days and bad days, talking about it, taking actions to support it and generally being more aware of the need to do those things, is the start of something pretty revolutionary in the world of work.

Hopefully, this book, and the images and stories around the inspirational people who are featured, will, in turn, inspire the reader. We had fun, laughs and shed a few tears making it.

All in the name of something we can all benefit from – taking time out. Let's Reset.

Neville Koopowitz

CHIEF EXECUTIVE OFFICER, VITALITY UK

One of the greatest challenges of living with a mental health condition today is people's attitude towards it. Misunderstandings and misinformation abound, and they fuel stigma.

The World Health Organisation estimates that over 300 million people worldwide suffer from some form of mental health condition, which can vary dramatically from more common issues such as anxiety and stress to more severe conditions such as depression, schizophrenia or bipolar disorder. Research from VitalityHealth's Britain's Healthiest Workplace study in 2018 has shown that approximately 60 per cent of UK employees surveyed are suffering from work-related stress or depression.

We've always taken a forward-thinking approach to mental health and wellbeing. We integrate support measures into all our plans to ensure anyone who needs help gets access to the support they need, whenever they need it. It's also why we recently launched a campaign to raise awareness of the issue of mental health, spearheaded by our Vitality Ambassador and rugby legend, Jonny Wilkinson.

In the campaign, Jonny reflects on one of the most challenging and public times in his life. His story is authentic and heartfelt, and, like many of the business leaders who have shared their incredible personal stories in this book, Jonny's hope is that, by sharing his story, he can help encourage others to look for support when they need it.

Collectively, the profiles in this book show that resilience isn't about weathering the storm or going it alone. Being able to reach out to others for support is an important part of bouncing back. Everyone's experience is different, but mental health is a universal challenge that we all need to be aware of. It's time for us to open our eyes to the issue and take positive action. Addressing mental health and wellbeing in a positive way is good for individuals, employers, and society as a whole.

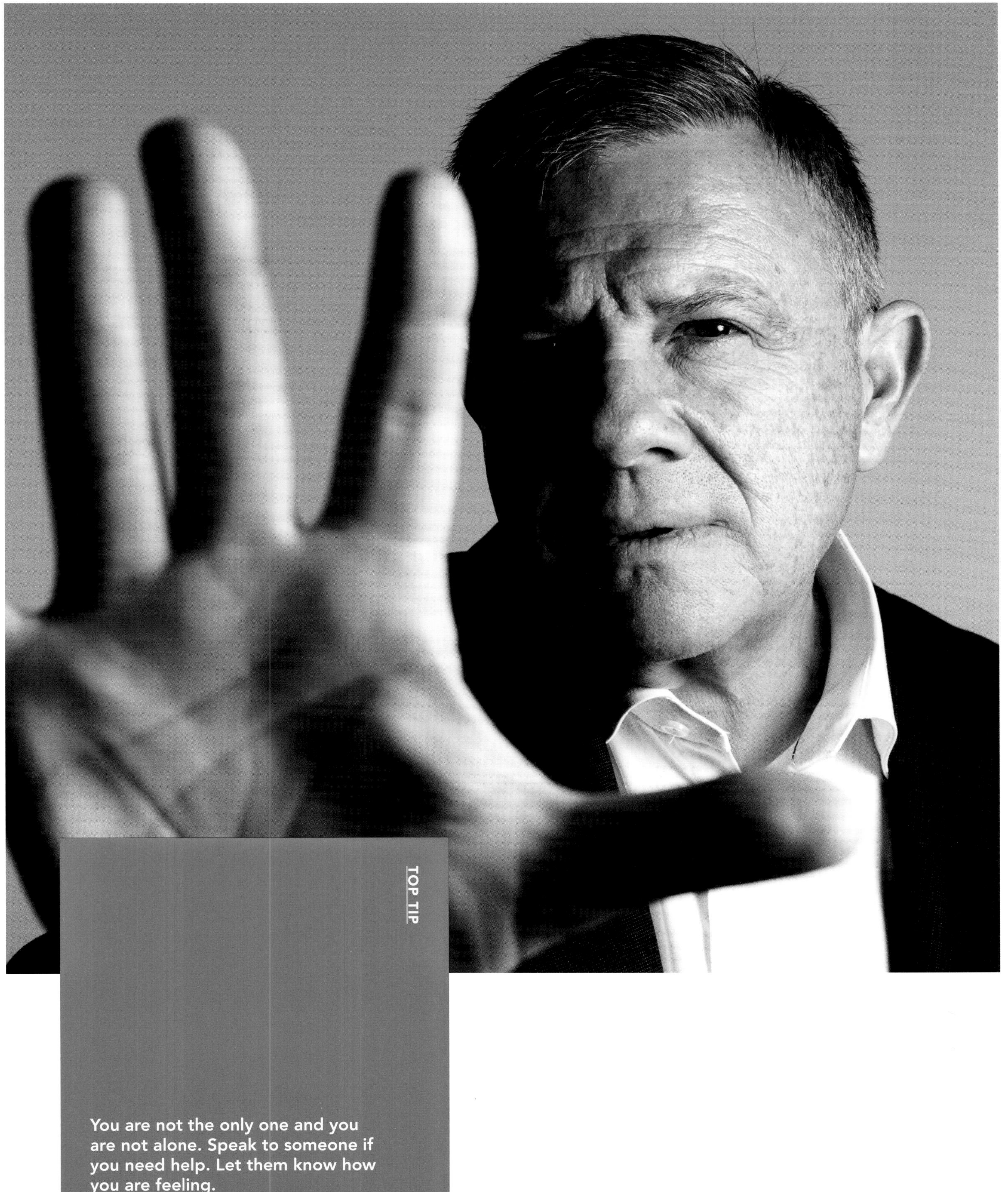

TOP TIP

You are not the only one and you are not alone. Speak to someone if you need help. Let them know how you are feeling.

Chapter one

Leaders with a personal story

STOP and bring your whole self to work

In this chapter, leaders talk openly about their own defining moments of liberation. For some it is an illness or a mental health issue, for others it has been an accident or a moment of self-realisation. For everyone, it has defined their life, provoked them to make changes and, for most, has had a significant impact on their leadership style.

Since starting work on Let's Reset, I have encountered all sorts of responses to the importance of changing the workplace. Many have been hugely supportive, but others have questioned what we're doing.

"We just had to suck it up when we were young, why can't people do that now?"

"The young are lazy!"

"Our key focus is revenue and profit, not human frailty."

"Millennials think it's all about bean bags and free food."

"I know that wellbeing and resilience are important, I just don't want to share my personal story."

"I don't know how best to help my people reach their potential and be commercially effective at the same time."

"This is so important, but I have no budget to allocate to my people to learn these skills."

And therein lies the challenge because the stats show that if we don't make this shift, we are heading for business crisis and I'm not just talking about Brexit.

I believe that in this new world, we as leaders need to be taught how to create environments that give people the confidence to walk into the working environment and be tested in different ways. We need to balance our 'game face' with authentic leadership that brings far more honest conversations! Fake news, like fake working environments, needs to change. Nancy Kline suggests in her book, More Time to Think, 'We haven't actually arrived in the room until every voice has been heard. We need to take time. We need to start by bringing our whole selves to work.'

I love this Rankin photo. He captures the strong, exuberant, confident leader in me, but, like the moon, you can only see one side of me. What makes me a successful and resilient leader is so much more; my role as a Mother, nurturing the wellbeing of two young adults; my three experiences and battles with cancer and the joy of being a mentor, learning from the next generation.

So this is why we have used very different pictures of leaders. Most of the shots, leaders would never post on their websites or publish in their annual reports. We have used pictures to illustrate how they truly feel, not all the time, but in moments of being vulnerable, angry, upset and happy. I believe that it's not until leaders bring their whole selves to work that we can begin to expect workplaces to change and evolve, encouraging everyone to share in a happier, healthier environment.

Lady Nicola Mendelsohn CBE

VICE PRESIDENT EUROPE THE MIDDLE EAST AND AFRICA, FACEBOOK

Some say that when something really bad happens to you, it's as if time stands still. For me, it was the complete opposite. When I was first told I had cancer, my mind raced to all the worst possibilities. How long did I have left? Would I see all my kids become adults? Would I get to meet my grandchildren?

I was diagnosed with follicular lymphoma, which is an incurable blood cancer, in November 2016. I was beyond shocked. As Facebook's Vice President for Europe, the Middle East and Africa, I was used to a life constantly on the move. I was young, energetic and I didn't even feel unwell. The only warning sign was a tiny lump in my groin that I had found a month earlier.

I lost half a stone in the three days after the diagnosis. I'm an optimistic person by nature but I had to dig deep to find the strength to carry on for myself and for my family. The survival rate for this type of cancer is variable, and I knew from the beginning I didn't want to give up working.

Of course, there have been hard moments, but the unbelievable kindness of people as well as more practical help makes a big difference. For example, I've been offered ginger sweets to help deal with nausea and lavender to help me sleep. Little moments which remind you that people are thinking of you. I'm also part of a brilliant Facebook group called Living with follicular lymphoma which is very inspiring and a source of strength.

At Facebook, everyone is encouraged to bring their authentic self to work which means different things to different people. Part of this for me is being honest about my cancer.

I've had two other CEOs get in touch privately to say they have the same cancer as me. I wonder what impact it has on a person to hide such a big thing? It never occurred to me that I wouldn't tell people. Many business people talk about having an illness, but if they do, they talk about it in the past tense. Why not be honest and upfront about it? Otherwise, we're creating an unattainable level of perfection. We're not being true to people and it puts stress on everyone in the organisation. We need to be able to have honest conversations in the workplace and remove that stress. Vulnerability in leadership is a crucial part of it.

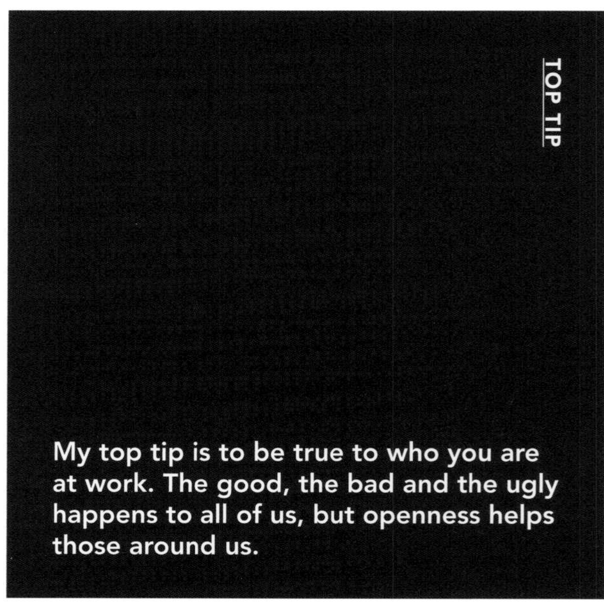

TOP TIP
My top tip is to be true to who you are at work. The good, the bad and the ugly happens to all of us, but openness helps those around us.

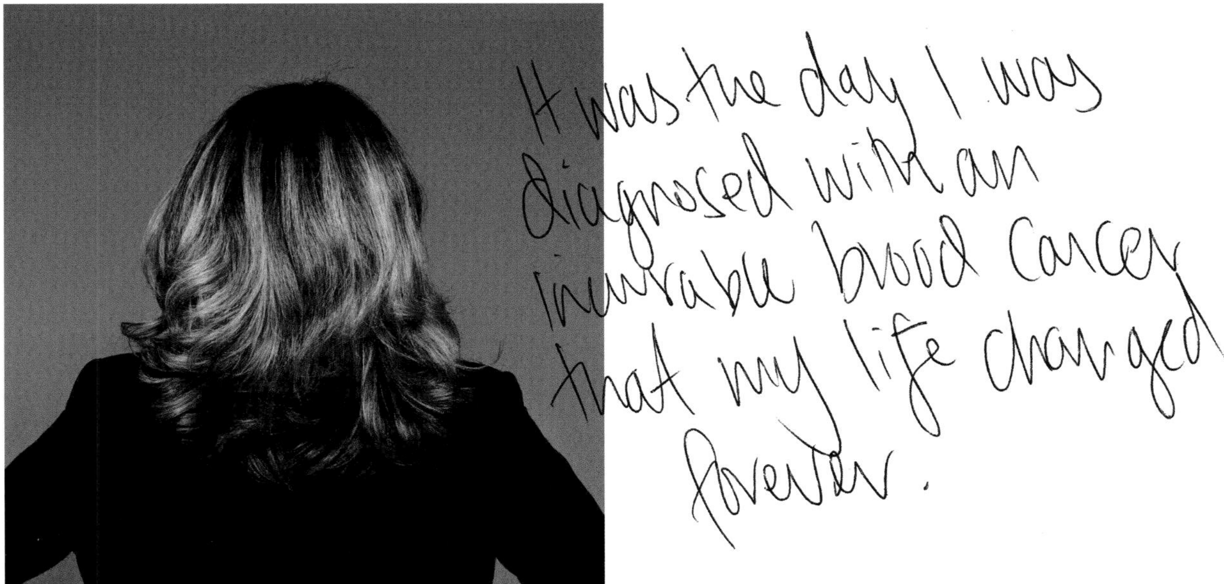
It was the day I was
diagnosed with an
incurable blood cancer
that my life changed
forever.

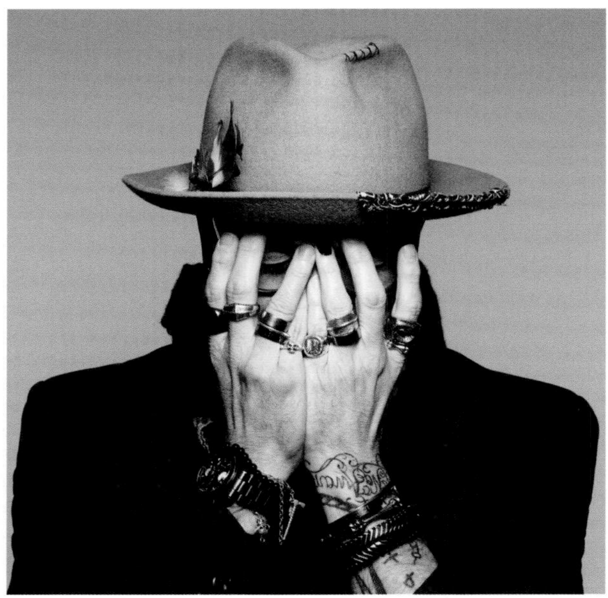

I have worked with Noah for over five years. He is creative, smart, fun and has a great sense of what makes a brand work creatively. I had no idea that he has Tourette's. I feel rather embarrassed that I had never made the time to ask, which is part of the reason this book exists. We need to make time to properly get to know people, it's not for us to judge but just to understand.

Noah Bernard

CHIEF EXECUTIVE OFFICER AND OWNER, SILAS JAMES | HEAD OF BRAND, SAMSUNG | HEAD OF BRAND, PRIDE LONDON

I have Tourette's syndrome. I don't walk around telling people I've got this thing. It's not a badge that I wear, but it has helped me to learn resilience as I need to keep it in check.

My version of it is pretty hard to ignore, it comes up in the form of hums and clicks. I was diagnosed in my late 20s. It was only when someone told me what it was that it came to life, but it has never impacted my ability to work. There is a blessing in everything as it heightens my ability to deal with things.

It's not something you know is happening and I have to challenge myself to be aware of it. I've learned to recognise the vibrations it creates and that triggers it for me. My partner gives me little signals so I realise it's happening. I am more aware of it in a business context when I am thinking a lot or extremely bored.

You have to accept it and understand that you aren't broken or that there is anything wrong with you. It has taught me to recognise that everyone has something going on and as soon as you realise that, it is easier to deal with it and understand where they are coming from.

I have learned to accept that this is who I am and it is my life. Acceptance was a big moment for me. I thought, 'Dude this is happening, how are you going to deal with it?' There are lots of ways: medicate, meditate, curl up in a ball, but I think you just need to find what works for you and embrace it. I work in a creative industry where multiple things are happening all the time, so I encounter challenges every day and I have to recover from them. To do this I like to swim; it makes me happy and comfortable, and I feel safe in the water. It is the one place I can escape and feel grounded and centred. If I need a break, being in the water is a spectacular thing. It makes me feel energised and ready to take on the next day's work challenges.

They didn't want a female Business Director on their account. Let alone a black one.

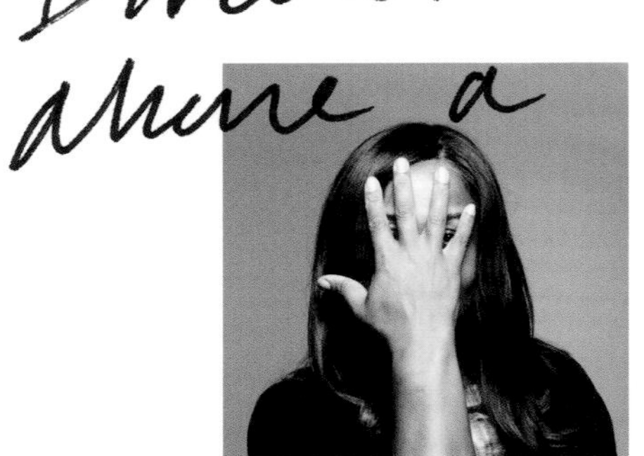

Just 11 per cent of women on Financial Times Stock Exchange (FTSE) boards are from Black, Asian or other minority ethnic backgrounds, so Karen is a valuable cheerleader for diversity across all organisations. She still experiences overt sexist and racist attitudes in the workplace. So much more work still needs to be done.

Karen Blackett OBE

WPP UK COUNTRY MANAGER | CHANCELLOR, UNIVERSITY OF PORTSMOUTH | RACE EQUALITY BUSINESS CHAMPION

I have seen a massive change in the past few years as more people have started to recognise the importance of a healthy and happy workforce and how it can deliver back to the company in terms of productivity, creativity and general profit. For Gen Z and millennials, it is a non-starter if a company doesn't focus on their people.

I believe that more companies need to incorporate mental health allies into the fabric of the business, as sometimes people just need to talk. Those conversations can stop problems down the line.

Being a minority in a workplace means I naturally have had to become resilient. I am still different from what 'normal' looks like. I am often the only woman in the room and definitely the only ethnic minority. Others look up to me and that can be a huge responsibility. I rock up day after day because I have an amazing network of cheerleaders; people to lift me up when I need it.

I was involved in a pitch a while ago and we lost. The winning agency took the client out for dinner fishing for information and what they found out really shocked me. They didn't want a female Business Director on their account, let alone a black one. I was so upset – it was so personal. You have to bounce back from things like that and get the verbal slap back from your cheerleaders to enable you to get up and carry on.

So many people try and live up to
an image that they think
others want them to be.
That is hard and stressful to do.
and I want people to feel they
can be themselves.

William Eccleshare

WORLDWIDE CEO, CLEAR CHANNEL OUTDOOR HOLDINGS | SENIOR INDEPENDENT DIRECTOR, CENTAUR MEDIA | NON-EXECUTIVE DIRECTOR, BRITVIC PLC

When I was 11, my elder sister was tragically killed and it was a trauma my family never spoke about. For ten years I agonised about it internally until I was in my early 20s and I realised it wasn't helping me and I needed to discuss how I felt to release the pain. This made such a difference and meant I was better able to cope with the other big event that happened later in my life. I lost my job when I was in my 40s and I had a family to provide for. I was completely honest about it and didn't hide anything, and I believe that approach got me through.

I am still learning all the time and I internalise the lessons to build my resilience. Early in my career I used to get angry with other people. It wasn't helping me to deal with those situations and I have managed my way through it and I have found coping mechanisms to grow and develop.

I encourage people to talk at work and to share their experiences. I try to make sure they bring their true selves to work and don't pretend to be something they aren't. So many people try and live up to an image that they think others want them to be. That it is hard and stressful to do and I want people to feel that they can be themselves.

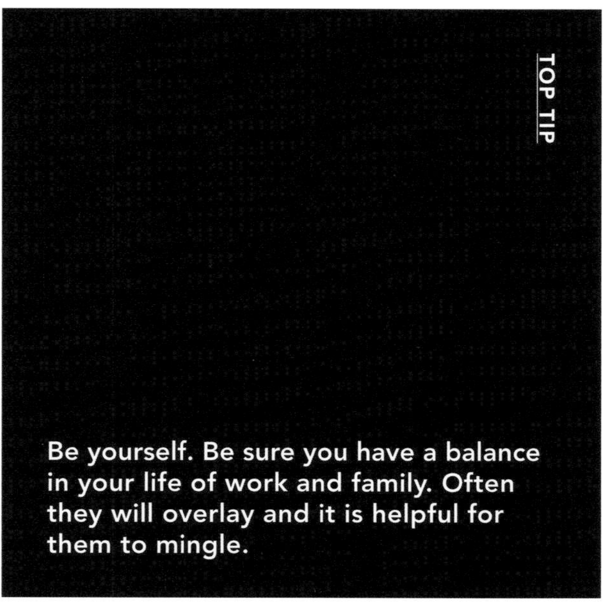

TOP TIP
Be yourself. Be sure you have a balance in your life of work and family. Often they will overlay and it is helpful for them to mingle.

TOP TIP

Own your differences. Don't hide them, don't fear them. Celebrate them and reveal them to everyone as they are what make you unique, memorable and truly awesome.

Nishma Robb

MARKETING DIRECTOR, GOOGLE

As a young girl growing up in London in the 1970s and 80s, I suffered badly from racial abuse. I can still recall being only seven years old and having to dodge the skinheads on their bikes just to get to school every day. Bricks were thrown through our windows and we were often called names and spat on.

My Dad, even at that young age, taught me to be strong and never to be scared. He would let me cry but would teach me how important it was to rise up every time I was knocked down. These life lessons have been crucial to me in my adult years. I was on my own from 18 and, living alone, with barely enough money to survive day-to-day, developed the strength and desire to succeed and the resilience to meet even the toughest of challenges.

Being a woman, and a person of colour, has meant that I have often been one-of-a-kind in many a meeting room or boardroom. However, rather than allow others' prejudices to hold me back, I have used my difference as my strength. That being said, I have, in recent years, talked about suffering from impostor syndrome – a term I have only recently learned, but a condition I have always suffered with. I realised that this condition was crushing any self-confidence I had, was leading to me over-working and, as a leader, meant that I was fostering this work ethic and continually striving for perfection from all those that worked with me. It was a dangerous, self-destructive condition. I had thought that my impostor syndrome was simply a factor of not having had a traditional route to work, and not being an Oxbridge graduate or from an elite, privileged background. These things I am sure all played a part in knocking my self-confidence – but without a doubt, the strongest factor has been the fact that my surroundings have never looked or felt familiar. This is why I believe company culture is crucial to improving the mental health and wellbeing of you, your employees and your colleagues. Creating cultures that are truly inclusive and set about embracing people from every walk of life, encouraging curiosity and understanding. These are the places that will survive and will allow talent to thrive.

Only 12 per cent of construction industry professional roles are filled by women. As someone who has led businesses both as a man and a woman, Toni's story is truly amazing and inspiring.

Antonia Belcher

CO-FOUNDER, MELLERSH AND HARDING BUILDING CONSULTANCY (MHBC)

I was born a boy and transitioned to a woman. I have been married to a woman for 38 years and I have children. I have always worked in the construction industry, firstly as a man and then as a woman. It is a male-dominated environment which has not been without challenges, particularly when I was transitioning.

Working in the construction industry as a woman has taught me the power of my authenticity. I have had to be resilient on a daily basis but I am probably one of the happiest trans people you could ever meet. I am a glass-half-full type of person; I would even go so far as to say glass-fully-full.

As a man in construction I was steered to be adversarial. I had to bullshit a lot, it was what was expected. But as a woman I don't want to do that. I believe being supportive and collaborative is a better way to be. We all have journeys and a need to be our true selves. You can't be collaborative if you are not your true self. There are not many trans people who talk about their true selves. The media want to portray them in a torrid way. My journey is positive and I hope that it helps others to understand. We only have one life and this is not a dress rehearsal. I don't want to be told how to live my life, I am going to live it my way.

We only have one
life and this is
not a dress rehearsal.

Anna Hill

SENIOR VICE PRESIDENT AND GENERAL MANAGER, WW UK
(FORMERLY KNOWN AS WEIGHT WATCHERS)

My greatest challenge at work has been when I have doubted myself, so much so that I have got myself into a state of panic. It is a common anxiety disorder when people think they are winging it. I worry when I have a big title, and ask myself, 'Can I wear it?'.

I have always had panic attacks and, on occasion, have frozen in front of a lot of people. There are voices inside me holding me back and I have to fight them. I have had coaching and hypnotism and I have got a lot better. When you have a weakness the easiest thing is to run away but I want to tackle mine. In my job roles, I present all the time and I have to confront it. I find it gets better, then worse, then better, so I put myself in challenging situations all the time to overcome it. I am improving, but I am not there yet. I find it helps to share this with my team and I am 100 per cent comfortable about doing so. The more honest I am as a leader, the more my team trust and identify with me.

Because I suffer from it so greatly, I think I am a good audience for others. I smile at them, nod and I look like I am engaged because I want to support them and make them feel good about themselves. In my new role at Weight Watchers it is all about bringing together physical and mental health. I want my team to feel that they really want to come into work.

TOP TIP

Step back and step out. Get perspective. Be honest and open and talk about your concerns with someone, anyone that looks like a good listener. Saying things out loud and being open can reduce stress. Leaders must be prepared to do this, so that everyone else feels it is OK.

I COULD EASILY HAVE DIED. BUT I DECIDED NOT TO. EVERYTHING IS A BATTLE OF THE MIND.

Matt Atkinson

CHIEF CUSTOMER OFFICER, CO-OP

On the last day of a solo cycling trip in Sumatra I was hit by a taxi. I cartwheeled over the front of my bike and onto the road. They drove off and left me to die. When I came round I was alone and had lost a lot of blood. I managed to stitch my own face up and freewheeled to the nearest town where, eventually, I found myself in an extended stay in hospital. I could easily have died, but I decided not to. Everything is a battle of the mind.

Having experienced a near-death situation which put my resilience to the test, every time I find myself up against a challenge, I think to myself, 'If you can survive that then there is little life will throw at you that you can't deal with'.

I took that mindset to my role at Tesco. The business was in transition and faced with big problems, not least 'Horsegate' which was the most public. We were getting it from all sides; external threats, internal pressure, the need for truth and what we could do to protect consumers. It was the ultimate call on my, and our, business resilience.

I think it's wrong that performance reviews in the workplace are all about objectives and outcomes. There are rarely questions relating to wellbeing. But to me that's a function of how you are. How much time as leaders do we put aside to see how people are doing? Most of us have people around us applying pressure and that pressure can create a positive or negative impact. At Co-op we are now building resilience and wellbeing into our performance reviews. We know from experience that it will make a positive difference.

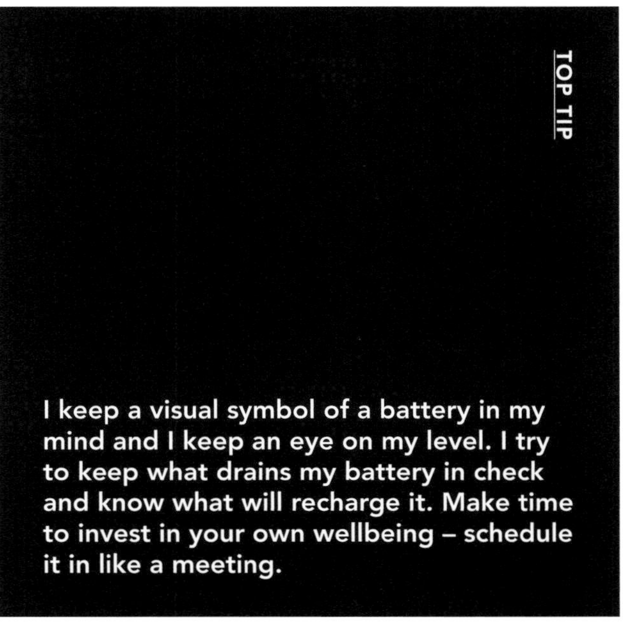

Dr Yvonne Thompson CBE FRSA

CHAIR, RADIO ACADEMY | FOUNDER, WINTRADE WEEK | ADVISORY BOARD MEMBER, FORTYSIX | STEERING COMMITTEE MEMBER, WOMEN'S EQUALITY PARTY UK | BOARD DIRECTOR, PUNCH RECORDS | SENIOR EXTERNAL ADVISOR, GSM | COMMITTEE MEMBER, ECONOMIC HONOURS COMMITTEE | CHAIR, AFRICA CARIBBEAN BUSINESS NETWORK

I started my career at CBS Records. I saw others move up the ranks and every time I applied for a promotion I didn't get it. So I took the leap and started the first black-owned PR agency. Back then, 35 years ago, the music industry was prejudiced against women and against black people.
I had a triple whammy because I was black, a woman and a single parent – the odds were against me.

People tried to put me off and I had to move up the ladder my own way. When things like that happen to me, it is my time to show what I am made of. It is about having self-belief. My success today has been based out of struggles. My birthstone is a diamond and my parents always told me I was a true diamond. As they are created out of stress, I believe I represent my birthstone very well.

In the Black community there are many firsts. I started the first Black Women in Business Network. We have just reconfigured it to have a truly rounded culture and now welcome all women. Black women in business have as much to learn from white women and the other way around and we all need to sit at the same table at the same time to help one another.

My birthstone is a diamond and my parents always told me I was a true diamond. As they are created out of stress, I believe I represent my birthstone very well.

TOP TIP

As women in business we need to build up our personal resilience account and tap into it as and when. You build this up through failure, and you must learn something from each failure and put it in your resilience account.

Use your emotional intelligence, it's amazing how many people don't. Find your focus and focus on the focus.

I was put into a induced
coma for six weeks.

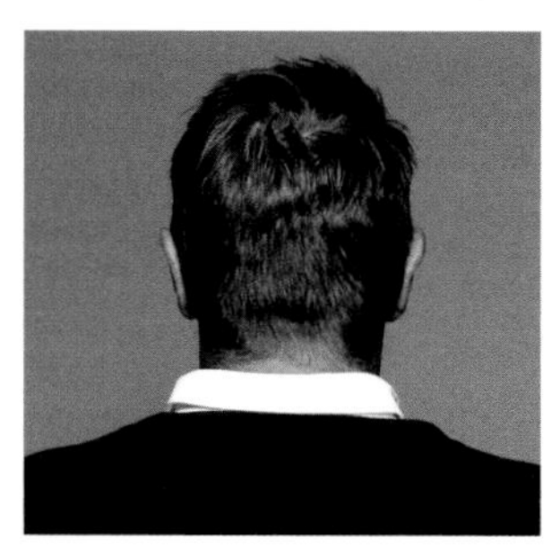

Gary Kibble

FORMER MARKETING DIRECTOR,
SAINSBURY'S, ARGOS

In 2009 I collapsed with a brain haemorrhage. Luckily, I was found, picked up by an ambulance, rushed to hospital and operated on that night. I was given a slim chance of survival and put in an induced coma for six weeks, then slowly moved from intensive care to a high dependency unit and ultimately back to the wards, where I was brought out of the coma. There was a long rehabilitation process to get back to living a normal life. As I got better, work consumed my thoughts. Not because I felt guilty or worried about my job, I just missed the structure and supporting the development of other people, not just thinking about myself. It took me a long time to get back to feeling the way I did before the incident, and that created a lot of mental, as well as physical, challenges for me.

Initially, I believed I was unbeatable. Nothing could get in my way and nothing could stop me because I survived an incident that would have killed most people. I was surely invincible. But I realised it's not always very healthy to have that mentality, and, gradually, I learned to develop a greater sense of immortality. I believe we only have one life, and we don't know how long we're here, so I live life to the full, but also maintain a balance. Like many people, work had taken over my life and I realised that my life was in equilibrium when I balanced my work with my family, so now I try to focus on that. I feel grateful for the wake-up call, which might sound strange to say right now, but my life in many ways is better for it.

TOP TIP

Always have integrity and humility.

Two of the most important words to me as a leader are integrity and humility. That means showing up to work, not wearing a mask and being who you are. It's really acknowledging that not everybody's going to like the real you, but also acknowledging that that's OK. Just being the best possible version of yourself is what you need to be.

You Need Girlfriends To Help You Through Difficult Times.

Sue Farr

SPECIAL ADVISOR, CHIME COMMUNICATIONS | NON-EXECUTIVE DIRECTOR, HELICAL PLC | NON-EXECUTIVE DIRECTOR, BRITISH AMERICAN TOBACCO

My resilience has been pushed to the limit several times in my life. The first time was a while back where there was a restructure in the organisation I was working in and I was on the wrong side of it. It was a case of fight or flight and I literally smiled and ran out the door. A few days later, it hit me and I fell apart. I saw a doctor and a therapist and got the help I needed; I just couldn't have struggled on without them, but I got through it and found another job.

The next time was when my first husband and I split up. It was really hard and I just wanted to hide from the world. I curled up under my duvet and cried and wouldn't answer the door. It was then that I realised the true value of my girlfriends. They banged on my door till eventually I opened it and they were able to help and support me. I discovered that you need girlfriends to help you through difficult times. We don't have to be perfect.

At Chime, our young female staff weren't getting the support they needed so we set up Grapevine. It started as a closed, women-only group where it was a safe space to talk and learn. We got successful women to talk about the things they had done to inspire the group and help them to find their own paths. It was created by stealth and now it is really established and guys want to come, but I tell them to set up their own group.

Work is only one of the many plates spinning in our li

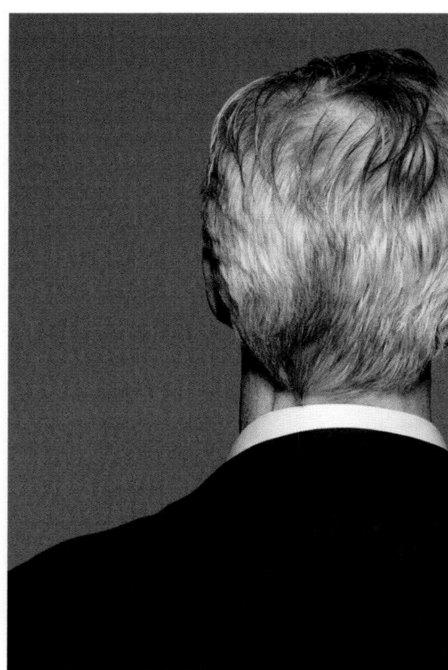

TOP TIP

I've always believed in the notion that in order to be resilient, you need balance and perspective. I often paraphrase Rudyard Kipling: "If you can meet success and failure and treat them both as impostors, then you are a balanced man, my son." In the creative industries I think we can drink too much 'Kool-Aid' following our successes, but also take it too personally when things don't go our way. Keeping a level-headed perspective about the 'impostors' is my key to personal resilience.

Russ Lidstone

GROUP CHIEF EXECUTIVE OFFICER, THE CREATIVE ENGAGEMENT GROUP

Following the premature death of my Dad over 20 years ago, I had regular and highly effective sessions with a grief counsellor. A metaphor my counsellor used during those sessions to describe my situation and how I felt, was the concept of 'emotional plate spinning'. For all of us, such 'plates' are likely to include family, relationships, work projects etc.

When a new plate, such as 'grief' or 'illness' is introduced, or an existing plate gets bigger, it becomes harder for us to keep the other plates spinning and it is possible that one or more will fall off their poles, figuratively speaking. My objective with the counsellor was to reduce the impact of the plate called 'grief', so I could continue spinning 'family', 'work', 'relationships' and 'friends' successfully.

Today I continue to use this powerful and simple notion as a way to think about the resilience and wellbeing of the people who work with me.

The inevitable blurring of life and work means that it is often difficult to separate or distinguish between the two worlds.

As an employer, I take our duty of care seriously. I'm very aware of the potential impact that work can have on mental and physical wellbeing. We support people who raise their hand as much as we possibly can and every new situation no matter how big or small, informs our thinking on wellbeing. It strengthens our commitment to initiatives such as partnering with Mind, employee assistance programmes, wellbeing courses, mental health at work training and beyond.

But I believe we have to think beyond our formal responsibility as an employer. To be a good modern leader, I think that we make a personal commitment to recognise when people need our understanding. This personal belief in recognising that work isn't the only plate spinning in someone's head, is not only the right thing to do – it is also key to a happier, more loyal and effective team.

Claudia Collingbourne

PARTNER, LET'S RESET

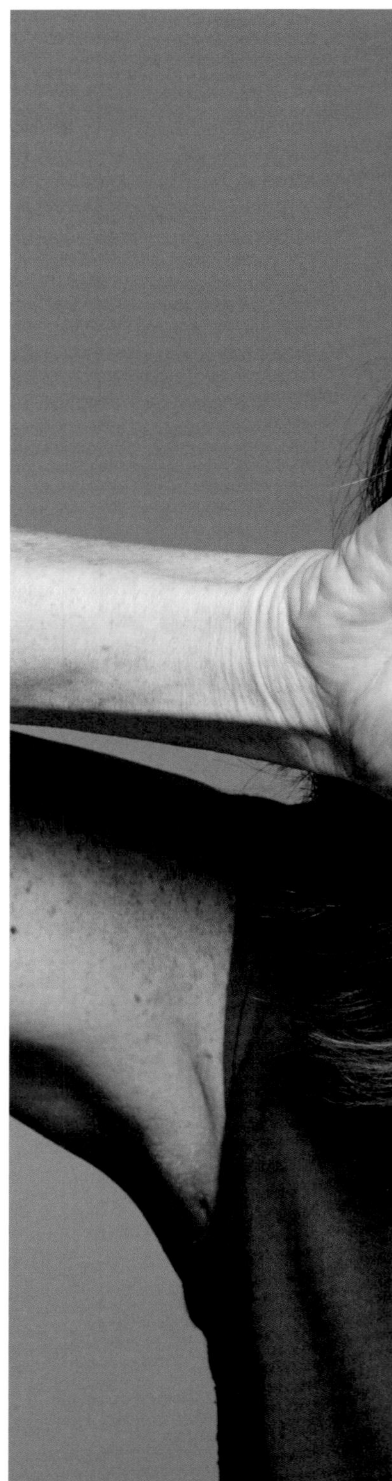

By the age of 13, I was an orphan. My mother died when I was seven, on the day she was to marry my would-be stepfather; a violent man who I never saw again. When I was 13, my father died from cancer, a gene which I too carry. I suddenly found myself alone in an unfamiliar country and reliant on the kindness of others, my stepmother in particular.

My father had been a high-profile music producer and I grew up in a world of celebrity. It was fun but shallow, as became blatantly apparent when he died and all our 'friends' simply vanished.

This traumatic and dramatic change in circumstances terrified me. There were times when I really struggled and would feel particularly alone. Christmas was one of them. I used to dread when everyone spent time with their families and I had to hope a friend would invite me to spend it with them. When I was at university, the very words 'I'm going home' cut straight to my heart because my student digs were my home. But, in time, it has all come good. I have my own family now, my career and friends, and I feel I am shining my brightest. It has taught me resilience. I learned very early on that I had to look after myself. I believe you have to make your own luck and seek out opportunities in your personal and working lives.

I joined Let's Reset because I'd like to help others to really thrive in the workplace, where we can spend so much of our lives. In the course of our work, we have met some amazing people, many of whom have had to overcome personal difficulties or tragedy in order to thrive in their work and shine in their careers. It's clearly possible; they've done it, I've done it too, we can all do it. We just need to face forward. I live by the words of the Red Hot Chili Peppers, 'This is not a dress rehearsal'.

TOP TIP

Laugh. LMFAO. From laughing with friends to watching silly cat videos. The act of laughing releases endorphins which improve mood and bring back balance. When things get tough, if, somehow, I can put myself into a situation where I laugh, I can re-evaluate where I have been and where I want get to. And I always try to remember, a smile is contagious.

By the age of 13 I was an Orphan.

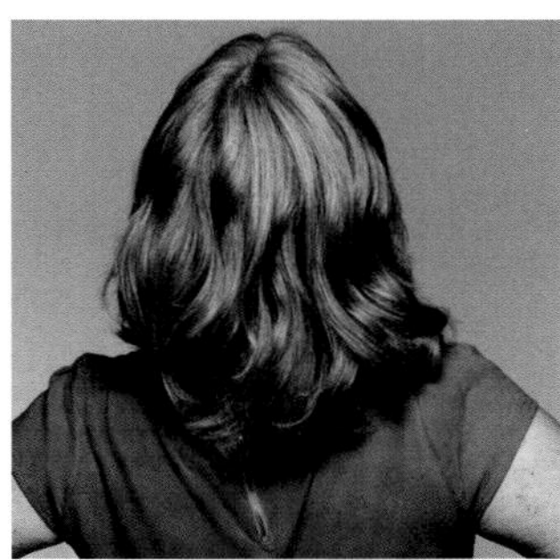

Michael Stephens

FORMER CREATIVE DIRECTOR, VIRGIN ATLANTIC

Labels have been something I have had to deal with my whole life, growing up as a gay child in a society that publicly promoted a negative vision of homosexuality – it was pretty tough. My family wholeheartedly believed they were doing the best for me. I didn't want to be labelled and I did everything I could to remove that, which meant not always being myself. You assume that people will become more open-minded as you move through uni and particularly if you move to London, but I didn't see that. I felt the need to identify myself as different. I can't say I have come out at work, it has always been a neutral environment for me. If they don't want me, then fuck them.

When you are growing up in an environment where you can't be yourself, you develop hypervigilance and perfectionism. You have a desire to control what you can, which can reap significant rewards, and allow you to progress at a fast pace. But what you don't see under the surface is that you apply those same judgements to yourself. Addiction and anxiety can come to the surface. I lived with an eating disorder, and still do to a certain extent. I am more aware of it now and can spot those moments as they start to appear – and there are still moments of weakness. I never went to anyone for help, which is why it went on for so long. It is imperative that businesses have neutral representatives who people can go to without judgement and bias to just talk. It often just starts with a conversation.

If you live in London you have constant opportunities and we move from one to another. There is a temptation to climb the ladder, reach for the stars. It's all about up, up, up, but we all need a moment to take a step back to breathe and process. Breathing has given me the most space and allowed me to see the wood for the trees.

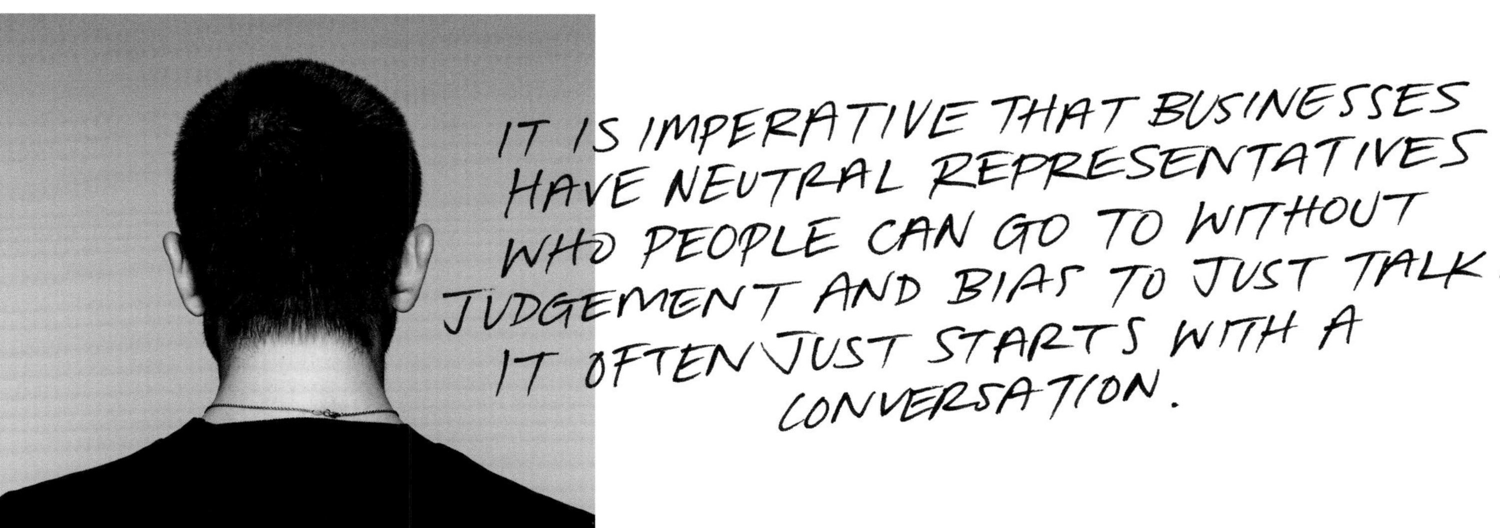
IT IS IMPERATIVE THAT BUSINESSES
HAVE NEUTRAL REPRESENTATIVES
WHO PEOPLE CAN GO TO WITHOUT
JUDGEMENT AND BIAS TO JUST TALK.
IT OFTEN JUST STARTS WITH A
CONVERSATION.

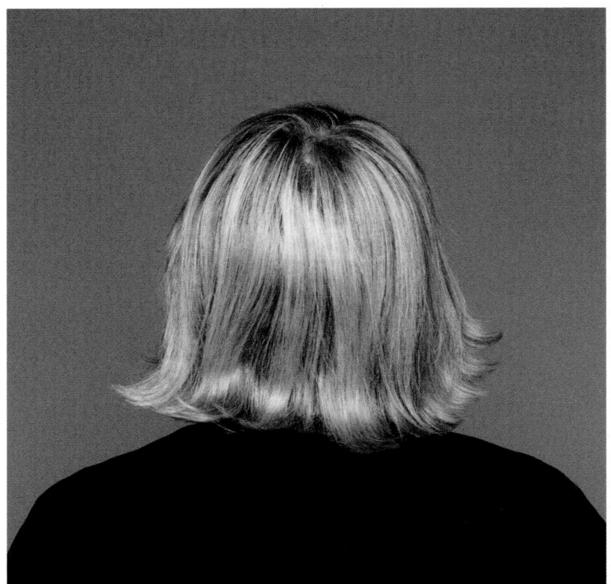

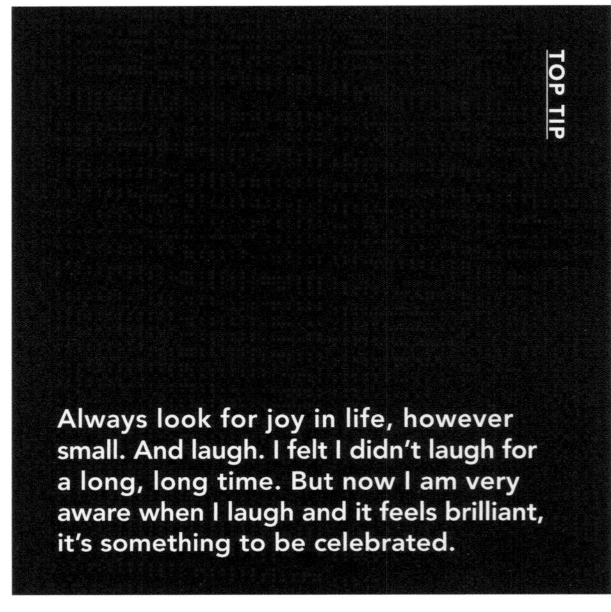

TOP TIP

Always look for joy in life, however small. And laugh. I felt I didn't laugh for a long, long time. But now I am very aware when I laugh and it feels brilliant, it's something to be celebrated.

Every night my Son and I tell each other three things we're grateful for.

Pippa Glucklich

CHIEF EXECUTIVE OFFICER, AMPLIFI UK AT DENTSU AEGIS NETWORK | FORMER PRESIDENT, WACL

One Thursday night three years ago I went to bed and my husband was there lying next to me. When I woke up the next morning he wasn't there. My life changed forever that day as he tragically took his own life. It was like a bomb went off. There was not a single facet of my life that it didn't touch. We had been together for 27 years, married for 21. It was, and is, really, really tough. I don't think I will ever get over the shock. Although I know now that it's true, I still somehow don't believe it really happened, not to us – it feels like an out of body experience. Suicide is now part of who I am and I wish more than anything that it wasn't.

I have asked myself a million times why he did it. He had always had low-level depression and I understand now that there are a number of different contributing factors. Typically, it's said there is some form of depression (be that underlying or very evident), combined with use of chemicals (alcohol or drugs) and then there's a trigger which causes it. In his case, he was having a really hard time at work and felt he couldn't find a way out of it. He could have done, but his identity was so tied up with work and, for men, that is often the case.

I chose to come back to work soon afterwards. I had time off for the funeral but I was worried as we were in the middle of a big pitch. I felt I had to be there and flew abroad for the final meeting. I thought I would be fine and able to get into work mode but on the plane on the way back I realised I couldn't cope. I couldn't just compartmentalise work and home so separately, they were inextricably intertwined. So much so, that after that I crashed and burned and then had to take three months off. I realised I couldn't be the same Pippa I had been – it wasn't who I was anymore. It has totally changed my priorities and outlook on life. In many ways I think it has made me a better leader. It has made me take much more time with our people. If we don't nurture our people and help them thrive, then we simply don't have a business. After Michael died, it brought it all into clearer focus. I don't want what my husband did to define me, but it has fundamentally changed me without a doubt.

On my first day in my new job here I told the team what had happened to me and how it made me view the world differently. I was surprised by how supportive they were. People say to me they can't imagine how I get out of bed every day but what choice do I have? I have good days and bad days. I often ask people when I start a meeting to give me their scores out of ten as to how they are feeling. They generally say, 'Eight' or 'Nine', but I will tell them it relates to their whole self, not just work, and encourage them to be honest. We are a team and here to support one another.

I'm still coming to terms with my loss. I try to be kind to myself and others. I can only do as much as I can do and, like all of us, too often put my 'game face' on to get through. Every night my son and I tell each other three things we are grateful for. Always simple things; our dog Digby usually features, or the sun was shining or something that made us laugh. Being thankful for the small things puts things in perspective and helps a lot.

So many companies say that their people are important, but just focus on the bottom line. Media is a tough industry; traditionally male-dominated, aggressive, results-focussed and stressful. So it is even more impressive that Josh has worked hard to put wellbeing and resilience at the heart of the agency.

what is the difference
between a psychosis
and a bad day at
the office?

Josh Krichefski

CHIEF EXECUTIVE OFFICER, EUROPE, MIDDLE EAST AND AFRICA, MEDIACOM

I realised that I couldn't switch off anymore. I love my job; it's a high-pressured, fast-moving and tough working environment and a bit of stress keeps us all going in a good way. But I realised that I was working too much. I couldn't switch off in the evenings and wanted to do something about that for myself and my staff.

I wanted to evolve the culture of Mediacom to ensure people could switch off at the end of the day and focus their attention on things that they love outside work. I wanted to give them a clear line of sight to have that freedom and clarity.

Our industry is young and mental health is becoming a bigger issue, so we have set up a programme to help people deal with some of the difficult things and facilitate building resilience. Sometimes things that aren't mental health problems are also misattributed. For instance, what is the difference between a psychosis and a bad day at the office?

Stress can sometimes be misunderstood as being a mental health issue. Don't get me wrong, stress and anxiety can lead to mental health issues, but stress alone is also often a fact of working life. So we have introduced training around conscious leadership designed to give us a better understanding of mental health, how to best manage our own state and that of our friends/colleagues and how to build resilience.

Another issue is the stigma around mental health. I wanted to destigmatise mental health, changing the way it is viewed and spoken about. At Mediacom, among other things, we introduced My Mental Health Stories where people write their personal stories and email them out to the wider company. It was a case of, 'This is my soul and I will bare it' and the people who did were very brave. When we introduced this initiative, it was a risk and we didn't know what the impact would be, positive or negative.

It changed the culture of the company overnight because people realised that they could talk about anything and wouldn't be judged. It received lots of support and opened lines of communication and took down barriers. Everyone felt safer to bring their true self to work. Now that we are building on this, wellbeing and resilience is at the soul of our business.

Steve Hatch

VICE PRESIDENT NORTHERN EUROPE, FACEBOOK

When I was 26 I experienced an episode of mania. I was travelling on my own, it was pre-mobile. A fellow traveller found me, managed to get some sense out of me and somehow contacted my family and I got back to the UK. I didn't find the experience of mania itself difficult. Strange though it sounds, some of it was really enjoyable, but the impact on my family and friends of seeing someone they loved act so differently and then reintegrate back into work, was hard.

The biggest barrier was the social stigma and the sense of embarrassment that I felt. If you have ever woken up with a hangover after not having been on your best behaviour the night before, it was like waking up with that realisation of, 'Did I really do that?'.

My reflection is that it was the most formative experience of my life outside of parenthood and I wouldn't change it even if I could. I also have an overwhelming sense of gratitude to my friends, family and the NHS. I decided to give back and worked on the mental health helpline, SANEline for four years, which turned out to be a great education in learning how to listen.

What I would love to be different is the societal context. We have made good progress to view mental health as a natural part of people's lives but there is so much more to be done. I understand that when something isn't visible, we respond to what we can see better than to things we can't.

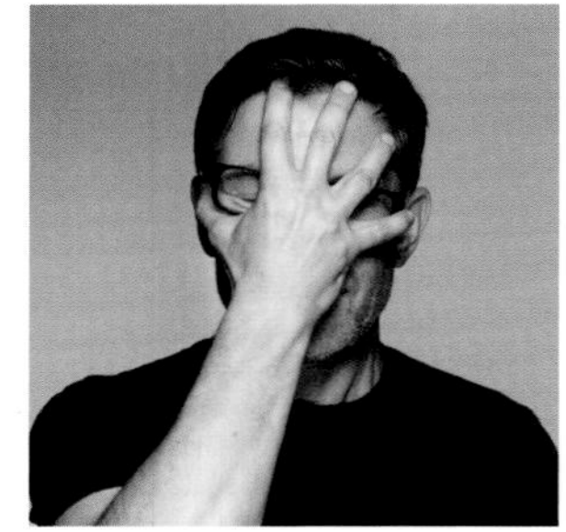

There is a degree of unpredictability but I feel really encouraged with the progress made by the differently abled community. For example, the 2012 Paralympics helped us to understand, celebrate and support that difference and the same should be true for mental health. There is a responsibility on us to make a change.

The biggest barrier was the
social stigma and the sense
of embarrassment that i felt.

Stevie Spring CBE

CHAIRMAN, MIND | CHAIRMAN, BRITISH COUNCIL
CHAIRMAN, COOP REMCO | CHAIRMAN, KINOMO

As for all of us, the ups and downs in my life have sometimes felt like riding a rollercoaster. But in the here and now, I feel a deep sense of contentment.

My mother suffered from severe bipolar disorder and left my family when I was just nine months old. My father's single-parenting skills – which included monthly family 'board meetings' to run our finances and discuss local and world issues – set my moral compass pointing due north from a very early age. From the age of 16, I have always volunteered or been a Trustee/Chairman of people-focussed organisations concurrent with my commercial career. Now I am the first non-expert to chair Mind. It's been a steep learning curve, but I increasingly consider myself an expert through lived experience.

It was only when I had a period of mental fragility that I became aware of actively managing my own wellbeing. It coincided with the menopause and huge work stress in the post-financial crisis fall out. Everything got on top of me. I had to prioritise 'me-time'. I started to run with my neighbour's dogs. Their adoration together with fresh air, getting grounded (literally feet on the ground) and making time for myself ensured I never felt completely overwhelmed. I am now an advocate for the benefits of physical wellbeing to mental wellbeing (and vice versa). I also have an active, if informal, peer support network of colleagues, friends and family and rarely feel stressed. I am learning to say, 'No' and buy myself time. But when you do, inevitably, experience stress, it's a truth that you can't cry and whistle. So, I choose to whistle.

It's particularly disempowering and, therefore, stressful when you feel you have no control of your own narrative. I have a same-sex partner which can be a big barrier to success in many industries, and, even more so, in many places. But it's always been important to me to live openly, bring my whole self to work, be true to myself and control my own narrative. We all need to be reassured that we have a choice. Weighing up those choices is a big part of getting it back together, because when we feel out of control we are at our most vulnerable. Taking back control of the agenda is probably one of the best things you can do for your wellbeing. I am a better boss, colleague and leader because I am aware of people's breaking points. If I think they are fragile, I try to intervene, make them self-aware and offer help. But it's their choice if they want to talk. Always ask twice how a colleague is feeling or coping.

When you are stressed
you can't cry and whistle,
so I choose to whistle.

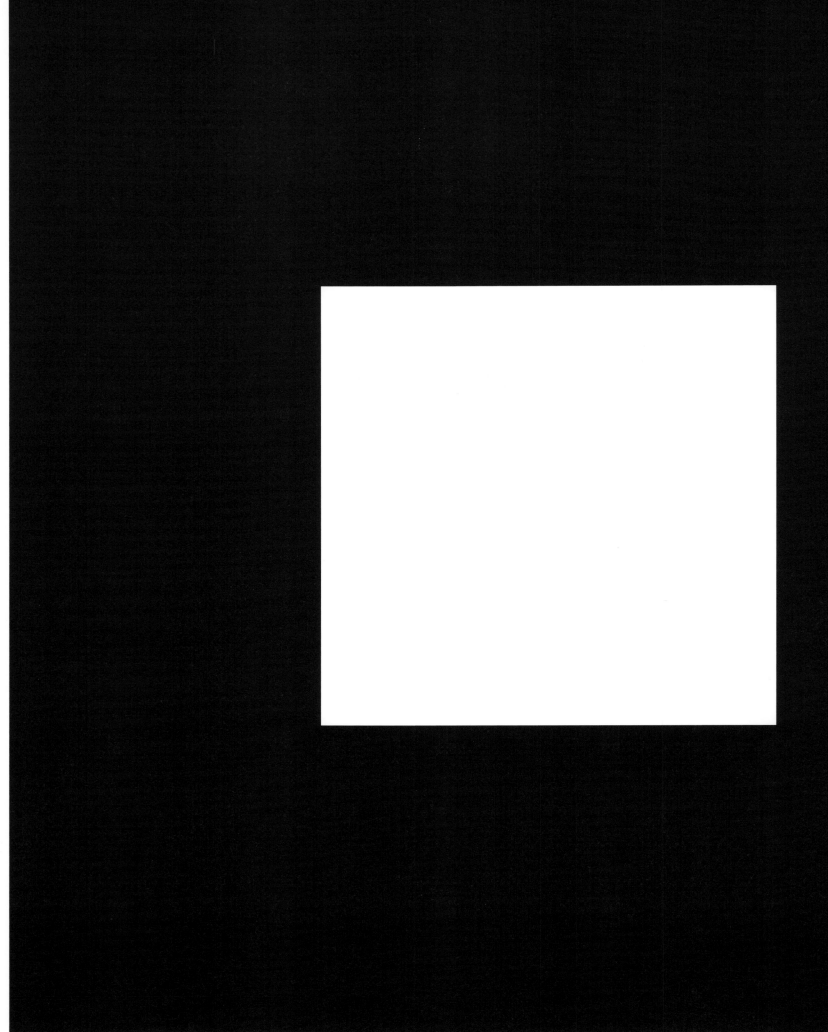

TOP TIPS

Stop hiding. Bring your whole self to work, take time to talk about who you really are in the workplace and listen to other people's stories.

ONE

Be honest with yourself, sometimes just stop and think, EBBOM: Engage Brain Before Opening Mouth.

TWO

Be true to who you are and do what comes naturally to you. If you're hiding things from people, they are not getting the best out of you and it is probably you who loses out.

THREE

Keep a visual symbol of a battery in your mind, notice what drains and charges it, then make time to invest in your own wellbeing; schedule it in like a meeting.

FOUR

Focus on the key things you can do something about and less on what you can't. Don't try to be perfect, there is no quick fix.

FIVE

Have the courage to push yourself a little bit too far, but the humility and self-awareness to pull back when you find you can't quite cope.

SIX

Tune out the noises in your head. Conquer 'imposter syndrome' and focus on what is really important.

SEVEN

Practice making decisions, so when it's really important you know how to really make a difference.

Chapter two

Leaders’ thoughts on wellbeing and resilience

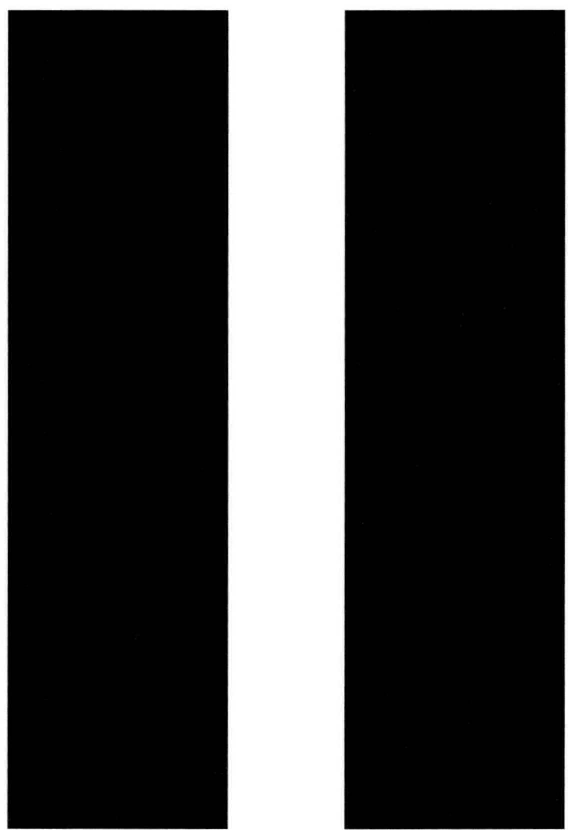

PAUSE and turn your back on FOMO

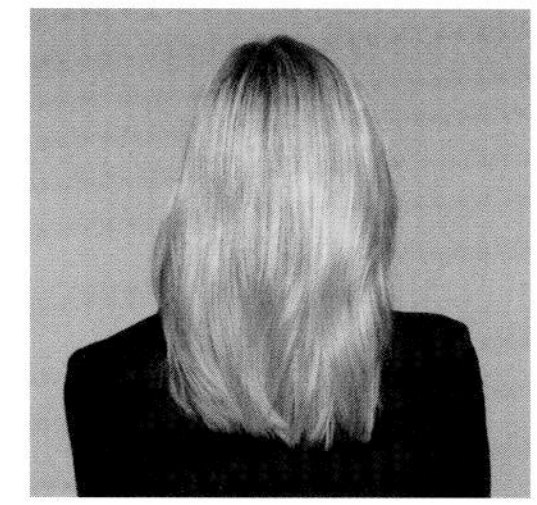

In this chapter, leaders talk about their own focus on resilience and wellbeing. One of the key visuals we use is the back of the head to represent FOMO. FOMO is a compulsive desire to experience something (or be somewhere) motivated not by what you gain, but rather by the fear of what you will potentially lose. And this idea of loss is usually (almost always) imagined.

A study from the University of British Columbia has found that 48 per cent of first year university students had less of a sense of social belonging and believed their peers to be more socially connected than they actually were. We associate FOMO with young people and social media, but it is just as prevalent in the workplace and across all ages; we just don't talk about it as much.

FOMO drives all sorts of behaviours at work. Sometimes effective, it can encourage a competitive edge, create the right kind of stress to get things done and empower people to try new things, but it can also be damaging. We all know that many meetings are unproductive, lack outcomes and productive next steps, yet we all fear that the meeting we miss will be the one where something amazing will happen and so our diaries are crammed full of meetings. The traditional culture where teams are rooted in the office while the boss is around, rather than being measured by their output, can be fuelled by FOMO.

On the other hand, there is no way that I could have run my businesses and been the Mum and friend that I wanted to be if it hadn't been for email, Linkedin, Google, texting, Zoom, Facebook etc. Research carried out by Michigan State University suggests that if social media were used for around 30 minutes a day, 63 per cent of people would be less likely to experience depression and anxiety. The research suggests that this is because social media makes it easier to stay in touch with extended family members and access health information.

We want, throughout the book, to give a sense of how to turn your back on FOMO and embrace LOMO (the Love Of Missing Out). Take back control, prioritise and focus. Many of the leaders we hear from highlight this as a route to their own wellbeing and resilience.

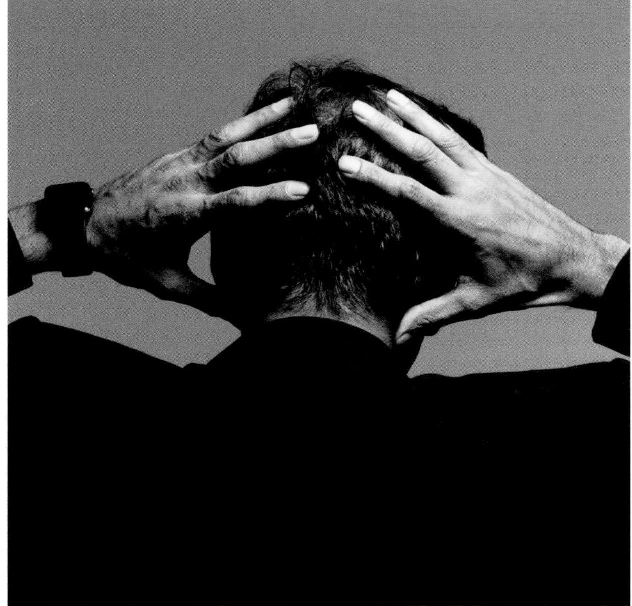

Deepak Jobanputra

DEPUTY CHIEF EXECUTIVE OFFICER OF VITALITYLIFE | CHAMPION OF THE VITALITY MENTAL HEALTH CHAMPS

Work is an important part of our lives. It's here we spend most of our time, how we earn an income, and where we forge significant relationships.

Sometimes work and life stresses get on top of us. Sometimes that's work-related and sometimes it's our health, our relationships or things happening around us. At times like these we may feel anxious, depressed or isolated. That's why, at Vitality, we're creating an environment where everyone feels supported every day.

All of our managers have had mental wellbeing training. Employees can also speak to one of the 75 Mental Health Champs we have in all our offices. Our Champs are trained volunteers from across the company who are easily identified by their mental health lanyards and desk stickers. They are always around to lend an ear and explain the support pathways available to those that need them.

Employees who prefer to speak to someone outside of the company also have a number of options. Big White Wall offers them free 24/7 support for a range of common mental health issues, including depression and anxiety. Our Employee Assistance Programme provides confidential telephone and face-to-face counselling. Employees can also access the Vitality Mental Health Panel through their private medical insurance, without a GP referral. Treatments range from face-to-face counselling and cognitive behaviour therapy to online guided therapy.

Through Vitality Healthy Mind, we also promote mental wellbeing as part of a holistic healthy lifestyle for all our employees. This means that everyone has access to helpful meditation and mindfulness techniques from Headspace, Buddhify, Calm and The Mindfulness App, too.

Our wellbeing strategy for employees focuses on physical, mental, financial and social wellbeing, and recognises the interplay between them. We have an annual calendar of events and campaigns focusing on all these wellbeing pillars, and tools and tips are also available on our intranet.

TOP TIP

Some people call mental health 'emotional health' or 'wellbeing' and it's just as important as good physical health. Put it on your to-do list.

who don't have thoughts about
ging wellbeing are dinosaurs
there is no place for them in
iness in the future.

Sarah Harbon

GENERAL MANAGER, BENEFIT COSMETICS

Resilience for me is about continuing to move forward. Business can be really difficult and will do everything to push us back, so being resilient is the only way to win. We need to be accepting of change. I have seen people so unable to change that they have been blocked from moving forward.

When I find my resilience dipping, I know it's because I haven't been listening to myself. At that point I know I have to take a step back. When I look at my life I can see if I'm not spending enough time with my family or friends, or on my own self-care. It can be tempting to focus on the problem at work, but often it is giving yourself time and space doing the things you love that will ultimately bring your resilience levels up so solutions become easier to find. We have to fill our own pots of good will; that is one of the biggest things we can do for ourselves.

There is a direct correlation, I think, between people's resilience and their personal wellbeing. Leaders who don't have thoughts about managing wellbeing are dinosaurs and there is no place for them in business in the future. It has to start with the culture of the business.

I want Benefit to be a lovely place to work, as well as meet our financial targets. We try and encourage a family feel so people know we have 'got their back'. We also have a Culture Club to look after our wellbeing, which does a number of things from putting daffodils on everyone's desk on the first day of spring to bringing in an ice cream van on a hot summer's day. It doesn't solve everything but it's always good to know that somewhere, someone cares.

David Dinsmore

CHIEF OPERATING OFFICER, NEWS UK

When I was Editor of The Sun, some members of staff were arrested. I saw people's lives turned upside down overnight. It was really difficult for everyone. A great deal of resilience was needed – it was an exceptionally hard time. We got through it and everyone ended up cleared, but they had to rebuild their lives after that which took time and was painful.

We tried to confront the issues as much as possible. The truth is it dominated our lives every day. It was over a long period of time and you could feel the pressure people were under. We tried to get expert help to minimise the impact but there was no silver-bullet cure. I have so much respect for all the people in the white-hot spotlight of it. You wouldn't wish it on your worst enemies. I work on the basis that tomorrow is always another day. If you run a marathon there are times when you don't think you can go on. But you will get to the end and, when you get there, you find you are not quite as sore as you thought you'd be. I try to focus on what I am trying to do. I am Scottish which makes you 'thrawn', as we say. It means obstinate – we don't give in to whatever is thrown at us. We all need support in one way or another. If your home life is not going well it is a miserable experience, and the same goes for work. If we don't support each other as humans we won't get results. Culture is the best way to get things to work and I try to create a culture of openness.

I am Scottish,
makes you 'thr
It means obstin
don't give in
is thrown at

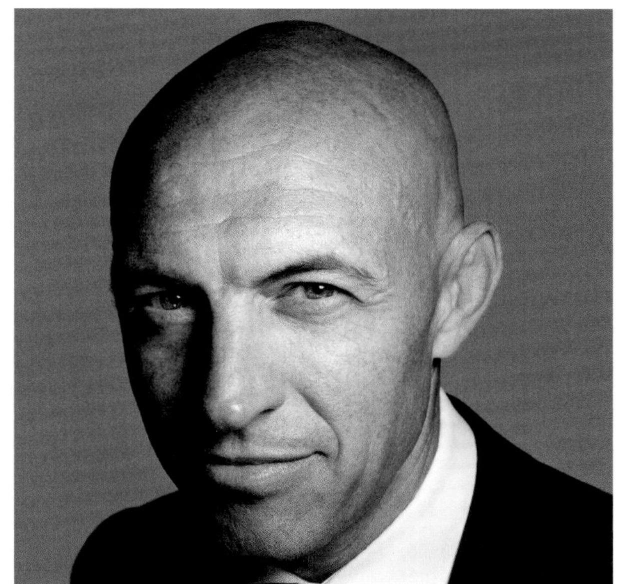

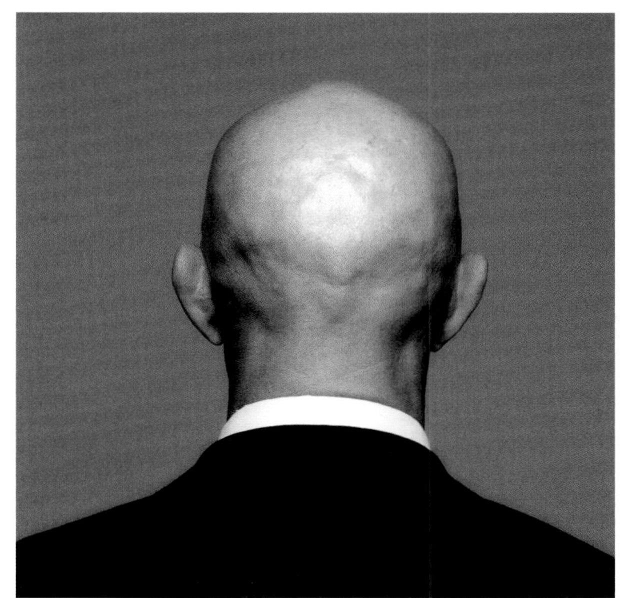

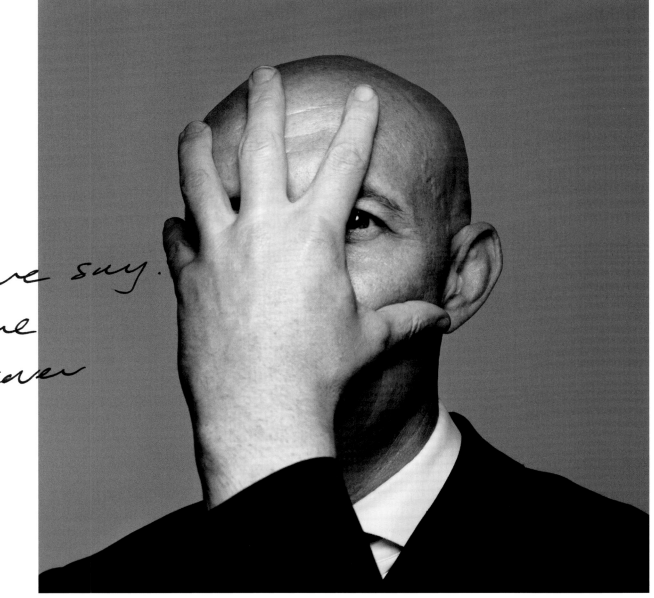

mich
in', as we say.
ate – me
'o whatever
us.

Amanda Mackenzie OBE

CHIEF EXECUTIVE OFFICER, BUSINESS IN THE COMMUNITY | NON-EXECUTIVE DIRECTOR, LLOYDS BANK

I love time to forget time. It is a peaceful and an important place to get to and spending time doing this means I can cope with just about anything that is thrown at me.

I like to stretch myself because the world gets bigger every time you do. I wanted to run a marathon seven years ago and I had regularly run three miles but it was the symbolism of running four miles for the first time which set me on the path to complete those 26 miles. We should all dare ourselves to do something a little bit more and then more again.

Having said that, it is important to try and not obsess about things that don't go according to plan. As women, we tend to have a 'judgment ticker tape' in our heads which can be destructive. Whatever happens, and to quote that line in the song, I always try to, 'Dust myself down and start all over again'.

When I get up on a weekend that hasn't got a commitment, I try to go where my energy takes me. If that means tidying my bedroom then I do but it if it means baking a cake then I will do that. There is something utterly precious about being able to meander through an afternoon with no obligations to anyone. People say, 'Be kind to yourself' and, for me, that is giving myself space, being alone and quiet.

At work I want to create an environment where people are listened to. When I ask how they are doing, I try and listen to their answer and notice if there are gaps. Gaps signal issues. It's so easy to fly past someone saying, 'I'm fine'. I'll try and ask if I missed something, which gives them permission to tell you more, and that is valuable feedback as to what's really going on.

Amanda grew up thinking she was going to be a doctor via the brief ambition of being a ballet dancer. She is one of the few Marketing Directors who has become a Chief Executive Officer. Her diary is very hectic and she is massively organised, so I was surprised and rather pleased to hear that, in her downtime, she likes to just forget time, something that we should perhaps all do.

TOP TIP

Sleep. Every day there is more science as to its benefits. If you look at a child who has gone without sleep, they are crabby and simply can't cope. As adults, we learn to mask those emotions but our bodies and our minds are suffering. I don't think any employer should expect people to work long hours week in, week out. Sleep helps people repair themselves. It is vital.

When things get tough, perspective is king. Take a deep breath and try a different angle.

Lindsay Pattison

CHIEF CLIENT OFFICER, WPP

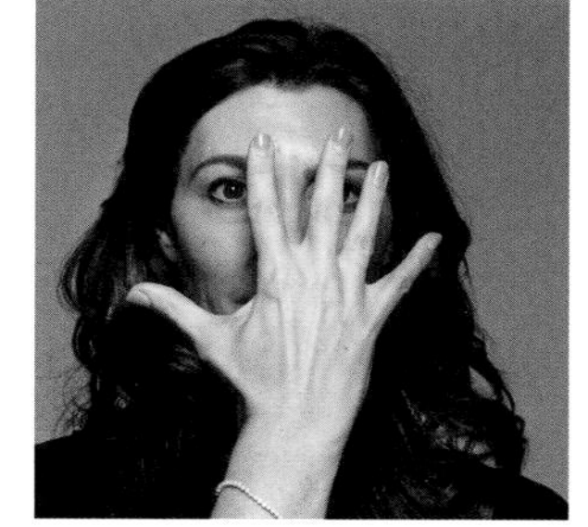

I live by a theory of three lenses. You need to look through each of them in a challenging situation. Take a breath and think about the lenses:

The reverse lens. How is the other person thinking or feeling about the issue? Get perspective.

The wide lens. Who else is thinking about the problem and what is the lateral view? Be less personal.

The long term lens. How much will it matter in six months' time?

I launched a programme at WPP in 2016 aimed specifically at senior women called Walk the Talk. It introduces the three lenses theory as a practical method but it also tackles barriers such as the voices in your head. We often encourage participants to lean on friends and mentors to help flip unhealthy perspectives. It's about identifying and building tools that support you. We don't need to be tough nuts, but we need to do more than just survive at work, we need to thrive.

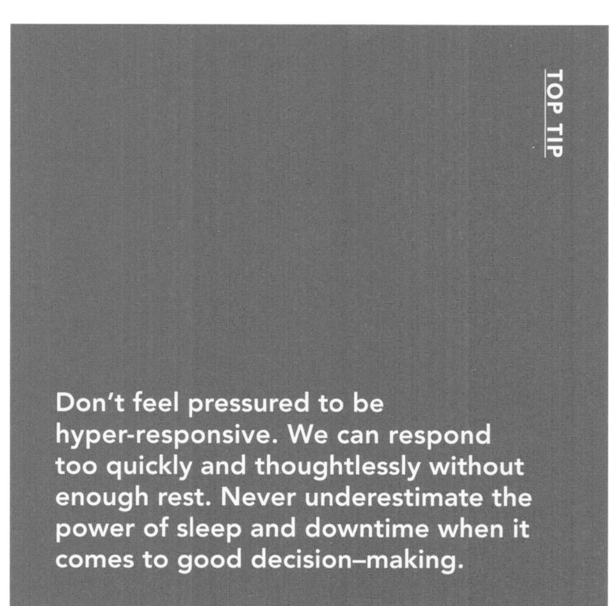

TOP TIP

Don't feel pressured to be hyper-responsive. We can respond too quickly and thoughtlessly without enough rest. Never underestimate the power of sleep and downtime when it comes to good decision-making.

Be a ra

diator, not a drain.

Rita Clifton CBE

NON-EXECUTIVE DIRECTOR, ASOS, NATIONWIDE, ASCENTIAL, BP CHAIR, BRANDCAP

I try and start out with a really positive frame of mind. I appreciate that for some people that's harder than it is for others, but by having a positive take on the world I can see the possibilities. I think it's important to be a radiator, not a drain, and I look to employ those sorts of people.

Of course, you have just got to experience quite a lot of shit from time to time. It helps that I have been around the block. The first time something bad happens to you at work or in life, you think it's the worst thing to have ever happened. But once you've experienced a few terrible situations, you know that the sun is going to rise again tomorrow and you know how to deal with it better the next time.

I use some neurolinguistic programming techniques to increase my resilience. I tend to run a video in my mind about how I would ideally like things to be. When I can see things in my mind's eye, it's easier to live it and to be it and to do it.

I like to create a work culture where people help others feel good about themselves, but nurturing people can also include tough love. For example, people sometimes need to hear that they are having a bad effect on others. If people are cynical and negative at work, it can poison the atmosphere for others. I encourage my leaders to get to the bottom of why people are spreading unhappiness, try and get to the root cause of the issue and help them with that. Ultimately, I want everyone to enjoy being the best they can be because everyone in a company lifts and rises through that.

Really smart people figure out how to achieve success and significance simultaneously

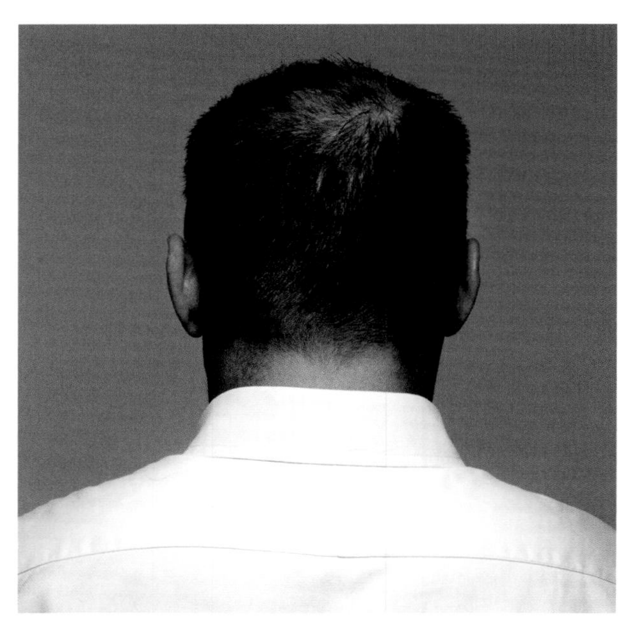

Mark Evans

MANAGING DIRECTOR MARKETING AND DIGITAL, CHIEF EXECUTIVE, DIRECT LINE GROUP

I have been made redundant four times and have never had the chance to resign in a 22-year career. I actually had a graduate job disappear in a puff of smoke before I had even started. These were tough moments and you might describe it as bad luck, but it has made me resilient and helped me to maintain a positive mindset because I have always managed to pivot into something better.

There was also a defining moment from the night of my graduation that helps me to keep a balanced perspective. A small group of us were out for a celebratory meal and my friend's father asked to say a few words. This is what he said:

"As I stand before you, I'm jealous. Jealous because, from this position, you can achieve almost anything in the world. But I also pity you because, for the next 20 years, you will go in search of success and then you'll realise it's not about success, it's about significance. However, the really smart people figure out how to achieve success and significance simultaneously".

His words haunted all of us, in a positive way, making us want to seek a life more meaningful.

Last year at Direct Line, we conducted a survey asking if people in the Marketing function had experienced a mental health issue in the previous year and I was initially quite shocked to learn that 1 in 2 had done so. As part of our approach to supporting our people and valuing them as one of our most important assets, we now have trained mental health first aiders in place across the business in recognition of how widespread mental health issues are.

There is a book that I grew up reading and often find myself referring back to. It's an easy read – Oh the Places You'll Go! by Dr Seuss. It's a children's book, but the message is as relevant to adults as it is to children: you will be brilliant, happy and fulfilled – not every day, week or month – but it's the undulations that give you energy.

TOP TIP

No rocket science – I think it's all about staying active. I see a direct link between exercise and wellbeing. I try to run three or four times a week and it's perhaps the only time that I can completely forget about work. Hence my tip would be to do something physical as an active distraction from stress.

Jacquie Mackenzie

GROUP HEAD OF HUMAN RESOURCES,
CENTAUR/XEIM

It is important to find a role and a business where the culture works for you, with people you can go to for support in your career or personal life. At Centaur, we have put in a few mechanisms. For example, we have a development board for the rising stars, whose mission is to find out what is important to the rest of the company. We have Wellbeing Week and we are training four people in mental first aid.

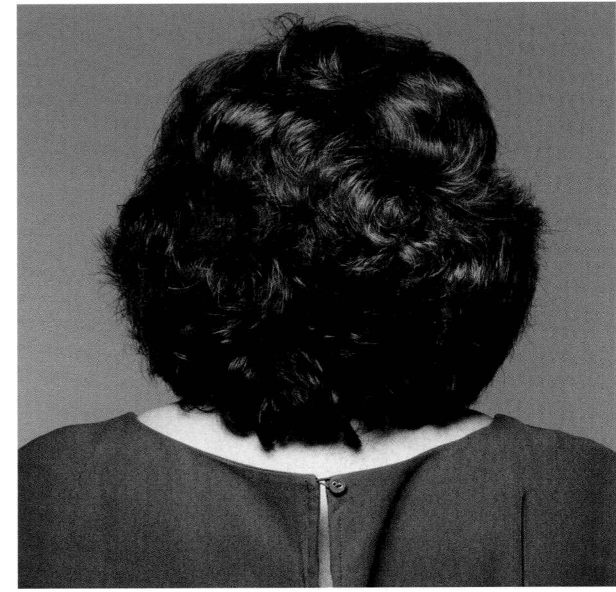

You are missing a trick if you don't focus on wellbeing. It seems to be the people you least expect to be the ones struggling – it is often the person who is the life and soul of the party. We have to look out for males of a certain age who, before, would never have said that they were struggling. Menopausal women too – there is a feeling of shut up and get on with it.

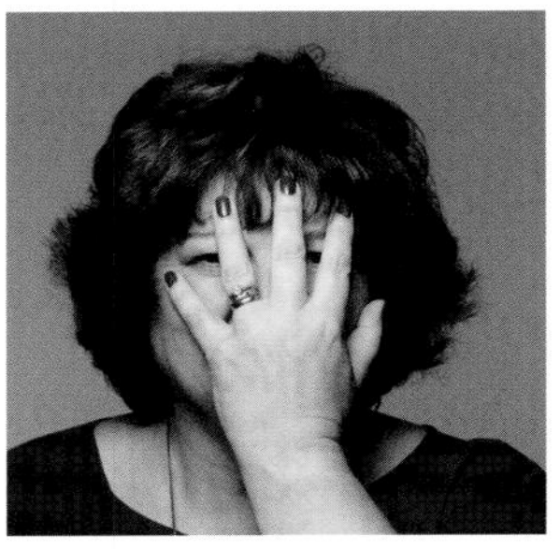

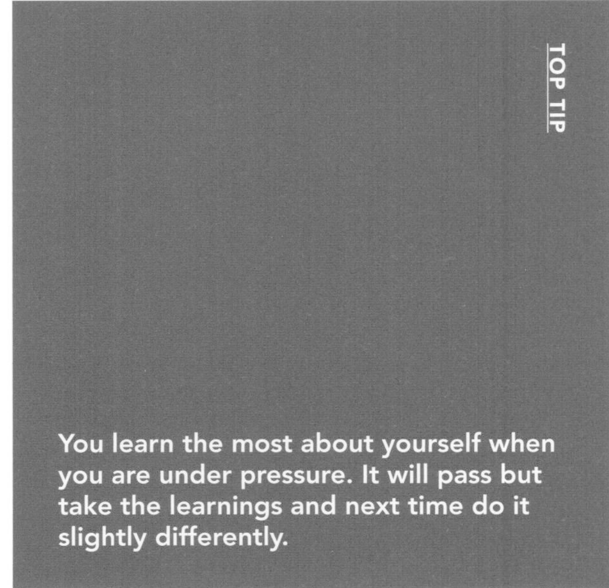

TOP TIP

You learn the most about yourself when you are under pressure. It will pass but take the learnings and next time do it slightly differently.

When the pressure intensifies, and you need to stay positive, I put on my 'Katy Perry face'.

Andria Vidler

CHIEF EXECUTIVE OFFICER, CENTAUR PLC

I am lucky to have worked in several businesses that have needed radical change. This has given me the opportunity to see a variety of management styles that leaders deploy to manage their teams through significant adjustments and transitions. I know that there will always be bumps in the road that no one could have foreseen and you may not have experienced before. Every challenge teaches you a little bit more. For example, in situations where there is a lot of change, people like to be managed more closely, with tighter deadlines and smaller projects. This is quite the opposite to when things are rocking and rolling, and they like more freedom.

Managing change requires resilience. Leaders need to build a strategy based on facts and then stick to it. When a plan hits an unforeseen obstacle and the pressure intensifies, leaders need to remain positive and demonstrate their commitment and conviction. I call it putting on my 'Katy Perry face' – the courage and commitment she showed to her team and fans during her world tour when her personal life was falling apart was awesome and inspiring.

TOP TIP

Treat yourself. I have learned not to feel guilty about taking 30 minutes to do something for me like having my hair blow-dried. It is a treat, but it also allows me clear time to think.

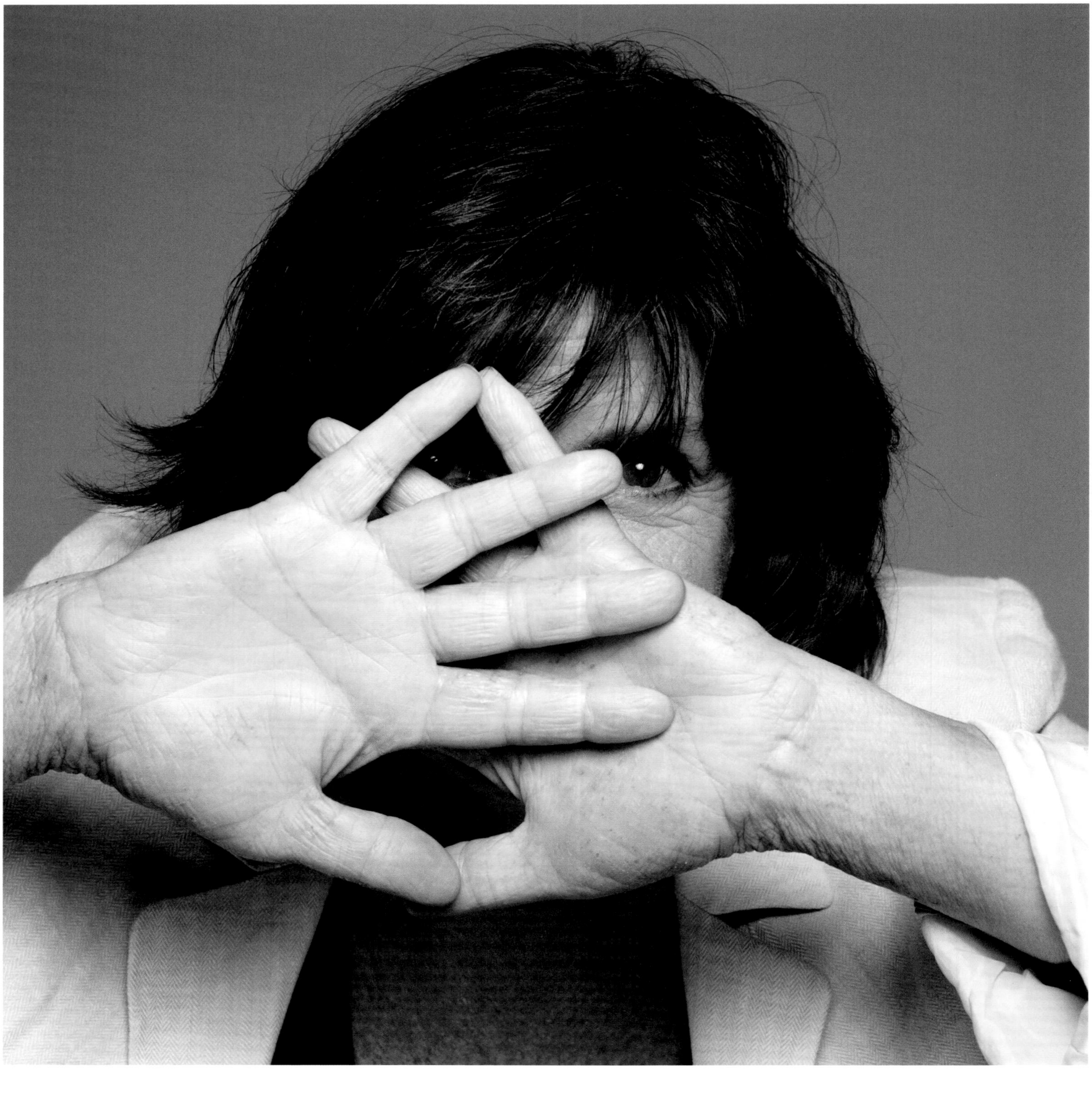

Rosie Pope

LEGAL AND BUSINESS AFFAIRS CONSULTANT, FUNDRAISER

Aged 16, my son Will was suddenly taken critically ill with end-stage heart failure. Kept alive with a heart pump, his only hope for a future was a heart transplant. During this stressful and traumatic time, with the mental health impact on Will and on my family, I needed to draw every ounce of strength I could. Finding something positive to bring out of it helped, whether campaigning for organ donation and fundraising for hospital equipment or thinking of ways to improve life for Will (and other patients) with the support of wonderful friends and brilliant hospital staff. I learned not to sweat the small stuff and to keep the end–goal in sight, drawing on my previous experience representing clients in my life as a lawyer.

I was lucky in not having to work during that difficult time, but the main thing that helped me keep strong and on track was the power of nature. Walking in the Chilterns was restorative, and it was pushing Will outside in a wheelchair on a crisp February day that really kick-started his recovery. Being outside made some part of him come alive again and regain the will to live. It gave me the strength to maintain a detached focus on what was best for him and a resolve in the face of the (often opposing) views of others.

Since that time, I have campaigned for organ donation and worked for the Royal Brompton & Harefield Hospitals Charity raising funds for equipment and now hospital gardens for patients, their families and staff, so that they can also benefit from being in nature.

For me, whether it's walking the dog or sitting on a park bench during a lunch hour, getting outside during the working day can clear my head. It allows me time to take a step back, gives me strength to keep the end goal in sight and the clarity to see a way through to it, whatever that goal may be.

I believe in allowing nature to give you inner strength and restore a sense of perspective.

By taking care of people you create better outcomes for the business.

Liz Moseley

FORMER CHIEF CUSTOMER OFFICER, WOLSELEY

I was lucky that, in the beginning of my career, I was able to have the conversation about being a woman in a male-dominated workplace. It was a very forward-thinking culture in both personal and business development. As a woman, I needed to work out how to engage in a macho environment.

The main challenge I faced was being first – the only woman in a 475 strong sales force. It's a bit like being the first born – the parents are learning as they go along. Sometimes everything goes well and other times they need time to work out how to get it right. I faced discrimination in significant ways. However, I have also had some exceptionally enlightened bosses, one gave me a promotion 20 years ago, when I was 6 months pregnant. Also, together with excellent HR teams, they experimented in flexible working with me, which was really enlightened in those days.

I feel very lucky that I worked for an organisation like 3M that really supported my development both personally and professionally. It is a strong, continuously learning organisation. Resilience training was an integral part of leadership development and this was vital to my success in the unchartered waters we were navigating.

I put great emphasis on ensuring my leadership teams always feel enabled to have conversations about their wellbeing. We explore what it means to them and create an environment where people feel listened to. I think we need to encourage more traditional execs to focus on wellbeing and understand how that can be monetised and how it ultimately creates more profitability. Many leaders still see it as people not toughening up, but by taking care of people you create better outcomes for the business. It isn't the most caring of reasons for creating the outcome in the first place, but if it gets us in the right place to get an excellent wellbeing programme across a business then, that's great.

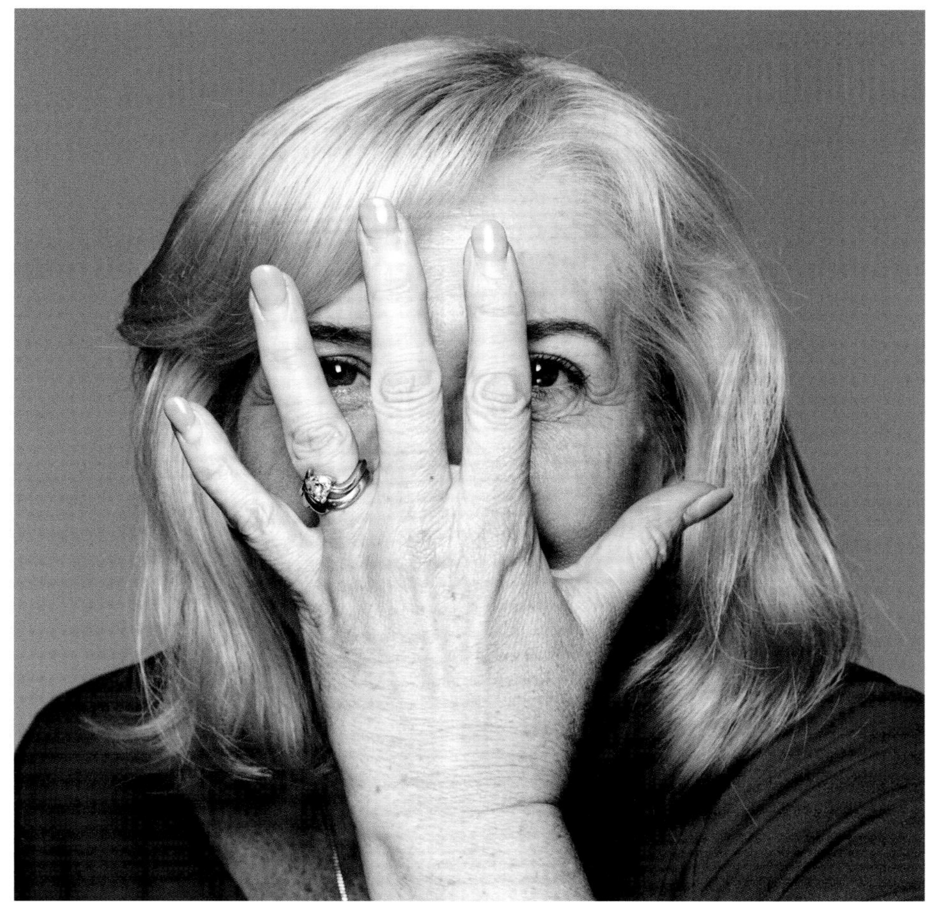

As a business leader it
on you to be brave
environment

David Wood

CHIEF EXECUTIVE OFFICER, WICKES

For me, resilience is a resource, an energy level that helps us face challenges big or small, simple or complex. However, our stock of resilience can get depleted day to day. This means that a leader needs to be both mindful and intentional in how they protect personal and team resilience levels, ensuring they create a confident and optimistic culture with alignment and clarity on both purpose and deliverables. A business will simply go much further and faster when all of its people are aligned and energised. The face we bring to work should be our complete self: authentic, humble and curious. To do this often requires courage, but the reward for this is the creation of an environment of bravery that inspires others.

is incumbent
d create an
f bravery.

Carole Stone CBE

RETIRED AUTHOR, RADIO AND TV BROADCASTER AND PRODUCER, YOUGOV | FOUNDER, THE CAROLE STONE FOUNDATION

Richard Lindley

RETIRED TV JOURNALIST, BROADCASTER

My husband, Richard Lindley, has been a television broadcaster for over 30 years on BBC Panorama and ITN News. Three years ago, we were told he possibly had Alzheimer's. Now, at 83 years old, his dementia has advanced. He walks very slowly, he shuffles, he has lost his sense of direction and more and more he forgets where things are in the house. He often says, 'I know I love you darling, but I can't remember your name'. Then he will look at me again intently and his face lights up as he recognises me.

He has had a lifetime of asking people around the world direct and searching questions about what they say and do. Although that sharp mind is no longer, he has established a podcast, Richard & Friends, as he still has the ability to have good conversations with friends and colleagues. He records in a sound studio in Soho, earphones on and stopwatch at the ready, which reminds him of his broadcasting days. His podcast was recently listed as one of the 100 Podcasts to Love in the Culture section of The Sunday Times.

It is a challenging time but a journey we are taking together, learning as we go along the road.

I have been a radio producer for many years, the former producer of BBC Radio 4's Any Questions? programme. I still work part-time at the market research company YouGov plc. The company accepts my slightly changed hours of work and

welcomes Richard to join me at the office or at the company's events at all times. This makes a huge difference because we can carry on sharing life together. Recently, we established The Carole Stone Foundation to encourage people to talk to each other, exchange ideas and make for a fairer society.

This autumn, we begin a Music for Dementia series over afternoon tea at the Concert Artistes Association (CAA) in Covent Garden. We can seat up to 70 people suffering with dementia together with their carers. We have a wonderful pianist, Tom Wakeley, to play film and classical music, and we will sing opera and theatre songs with different singers on every occasion. Social contact, music, laughter and conversation all contribute to keeping Richard and I optimistic.

We have had difficult times, but we have also had love and warmth from our good friends and also from complete strangers who give up their seats and stretch out their hands to steady a wobbly moment and just share a smile.

I have a benchmark that I use,
which is that on my deathbed,
If I am going to regret something,
I won't do it no matter what it is.
The cost to myself is too great.

Anna Sofat

FOUNDER, ADDIDI WEALTH | FOUNDER, #AREYOUIN MOVEMENT

I work in the male-dominated world of finance. The industry is one of the biggest employers in the UK but it is broken. It has the biggest pay gap, it underserves women and it is riddled with mis-selling.

As a youngster in this industry, I soon realised that, if you wanted to climb the corporate ladder, you had to step over people and be ruthless – it was pretty ugly. At some level, I understood that, if this was what it took to be a success then it would kill who I am and I instinctively stepped back.

There was another point when I was under so much stress that I woke up one morning crying. I was near breaking point and I had to re-evaluate who I was. I left and set up Addidi. It is my business so I can control the environment.

I created my business specifically for women as many are disengaged with the finance industry. I believe the yin yang balance is really important and that there is a fine line between being in a dark place or in a good place. I try hard to focus on the positives; I protect myself and I am mindful about those around me, my clients and my staff.

I believe you have to tune out the noises in your head and focus on what is really important to you as a person. I have a benchmark that I use, which is that if I think I am going to regret something on my deathbed, I won't do it no matter what it is. The cost to myself is too great.

This is why I have recently founded the #AreYouIn movement to bring about cultural change within the finance industry. I knew if I didn't at least try, I would regret it.

Feilim Mackle

NON-EXECUTIVE DIRECTOR CHAIR, ARDONAGH GROUP | TRUSTEE, MACMILLAN CANCER SUPPORT

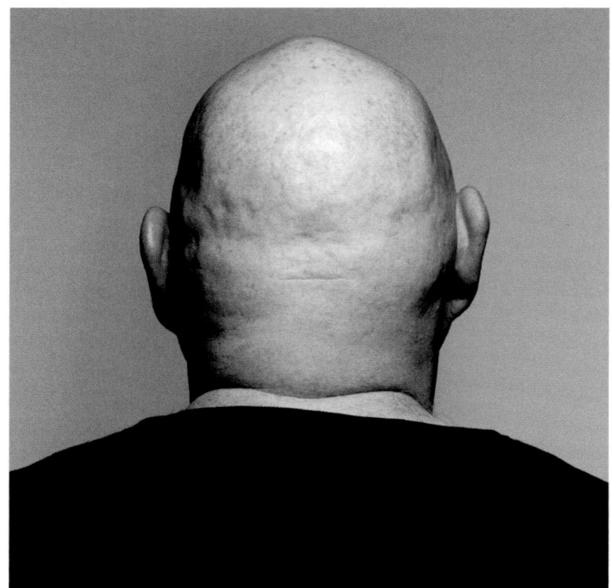

Our lives are full of clutter and noise, deadlines and meetings, notifications and demands. Approaching this busy life with curiosity, energy, rigour and a strong sense of what matters most can help you build inner resilience and have a positive impact on others.

I believe it's important to travel lots, laugh often, cry when you feel like it, be ruthless with your time, build strong relationships, create outstanding teams, surround yourself with people who are different like you, reset often, obsess about your customers and your colleagues, show vulnerability, celebrate success, call out bad behaviour, spend quality time on your own, support others and bring your best self to every aspect of life.

I have had the privilege of creating, inheriting and working with extraordinary teams and leaders across several sectors. In the midst of thousands of employees, millions of customers and billions of pounds across banking, insurance and telco, one area has repeatedly stood out. The importance of creating an environment where people feel truly empowered and supported to deliver the very best outcomes for customers. This is what matters the most.

Love what you do. Only four words, but they were the seeds for a truly transformational change across 500 retail stores led by an inspiring leader in my team. It created such a buzz and amazing environment. Our people and customers loved it and, funnily enough shareholders were happy also.

As I slowly mature it's dawned on me that the next chapter for those of us trying to inspire others is not yet written. Go grab it and make it happen.

LIVE LIFE, LOVE LIFE, ENJOY LIFE.
ONLY SIX WORDS, OFTEN USED,
BUT SO, SO IMPORTANT.

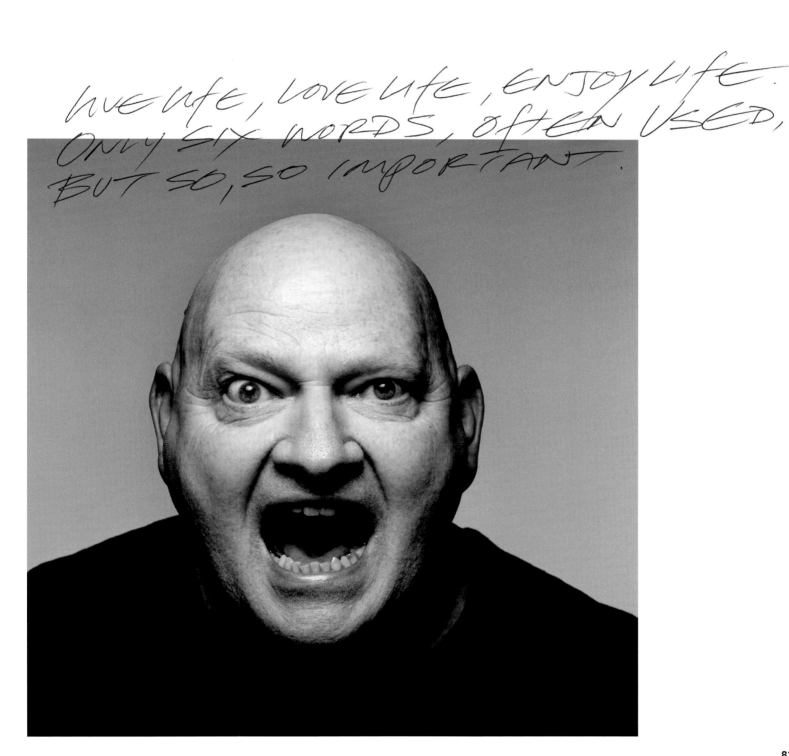

HEALTH IS THE MOST IMPORTANT THING
WE NEED TO MAKE CONVERSATIONS A
HEALTH AND WELLBEING THE NORM
BECOME EMBEDDED IN OUR DAY-TO-

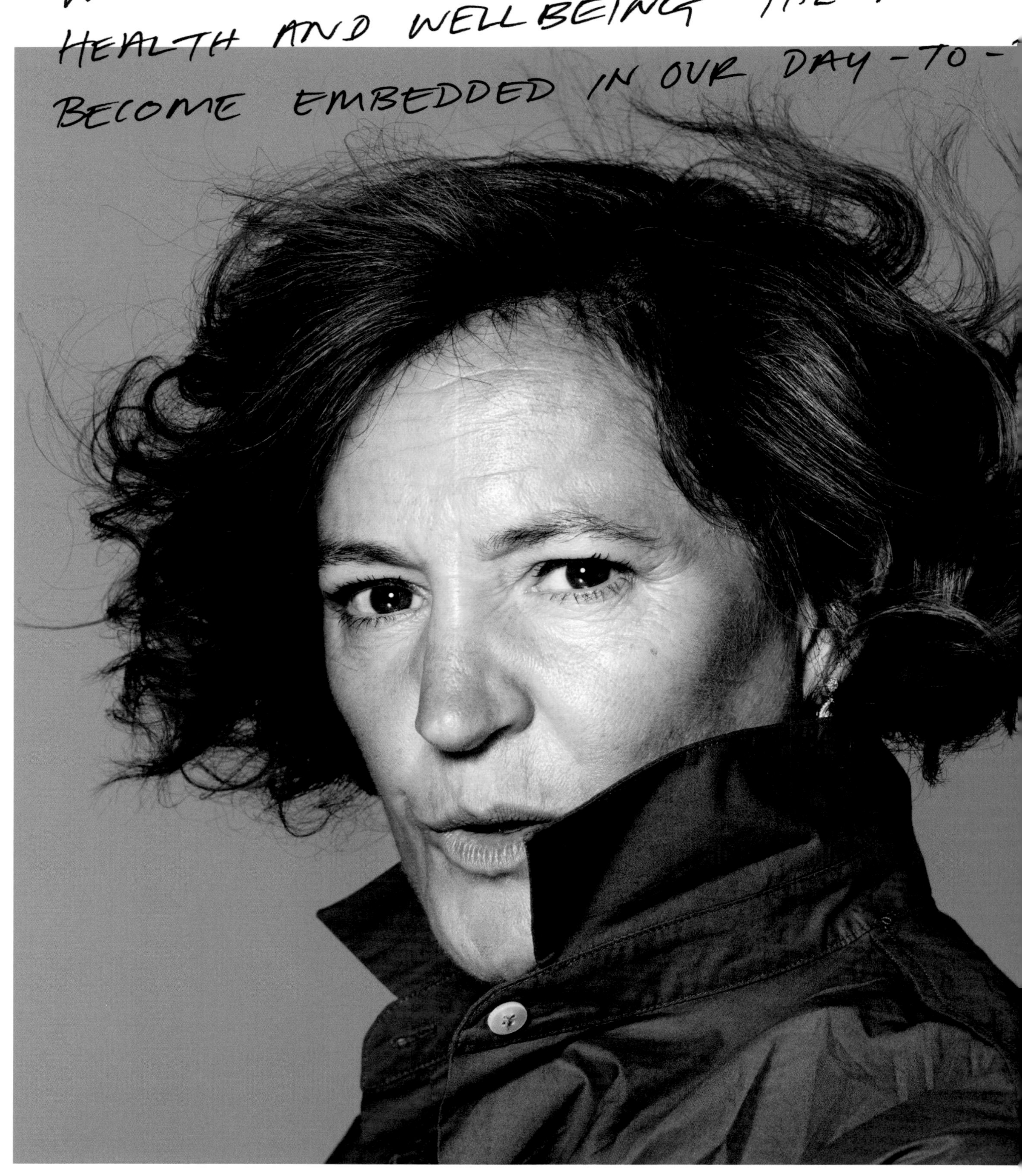

WE HAVE .
OUT MENTAL
SO THAT THEY
Y CULTURE.

Annette King

CHIEF EXECUTIVE OFFICER, PUBLICIS GROUPE UK

The world of advertising can be as tough as it is rewarding, and we need to help our people deal with this and find ways to thrive on a daily basis. Tough can come in different forms; extreme spikes in workload around a client's needs, pitches that don't convert or the great idea that never quite made it, to name a few examples. We need to find ways to help our people to develop their resilience and cope on the days when tough is really tough, so that they can enjoy the many great days.

Mental health has always been important to me and when I started at Publicis Groupe UK, I was happy to be approached by our Publicis Health President, Philip Chin, who asked me to consider developing a robust programme for the Groupe. I am responsible for over 5,000 people in the UK so this was an easy decision to make. Since then, we've put a lot of effort into developing a mental health programme called Headline which covers many aspects of what we need to do, from proactively spotting mental health issues before they get out of control right through to making sure we are getting the most out of our health insurance.

Across the business, we now have support from 97 mental health first-aiders, 132 mental health and wellbeing ambassadors and 442 people who have attended training on stress awareness and mental health in the workplace. On top of this, we are asking our people to take a day back for themselves on Global Mental Health Day this year to focus on their self-care or the care of someone else throughout our own Mental Health Awareness Week, when we will host events and support across our key UK campuses. We will not solve this issue overnight, but I strongly believe that the more we make mental health and wellbeing a norm in the workplace and approach it in a human way, the more we will help destigmatise it and embed it in our day-to-day culture.

Helen Gorman

CHIEF MARKETING OFFICER, FTSE COMPANIES | OYSTERCATCHERS CONSULTANCY

I have spent over 20 years of my career leading marketing teams in FTSE 200 companies. One of my early observations was how I was going to look after and stay true to myself, while delivering commercial growth in tough, challenging environments.

Delivering growth in business today is tougher than ever. I've realised that I'm at my best when I balance time between work and the people and things that I love outside of work. The tougher the work challenge, the more important this is for me to perform well and lead others to do so too. As I've grown older and more experienced, I have seen how important and beneficial it is to encourage yourself and those who work around you not to get consumed by work but to get some outside perspective and feed your own wellbeing with the things that make you feel great.

I have built my own resilience through the challenges that life has brought both inside and outside of work. From the repetitive challenges of the boardroom, to the biggest resilience challenge of all in fighting a three-year battle with cancer in my early thirties. When it's life and death, you quickly work out what matters and I'm lucky that has stayed with me. My current challenge of raising two teenage boys and navigating their wellbeing in the modern world makes me passionate about helping to create a real place for wellbeing in the workplace.

The next generation workforce is growing up in an educational environment where building resilience and wellbeing is fast becoming the norm. I firmly believe that it will be the businesses that really start to embrace and embed this in their culture, that will attract the future talent and grow.

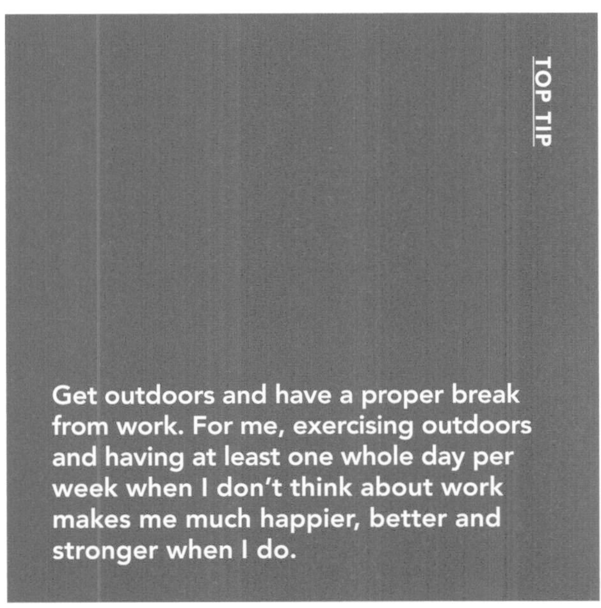

TOP TIP

Get outdoors and have a proper break from work. For me, exercising outdoors and having at least one whole day per week when I don't think about work makes me much happier, better and stronger when I do.

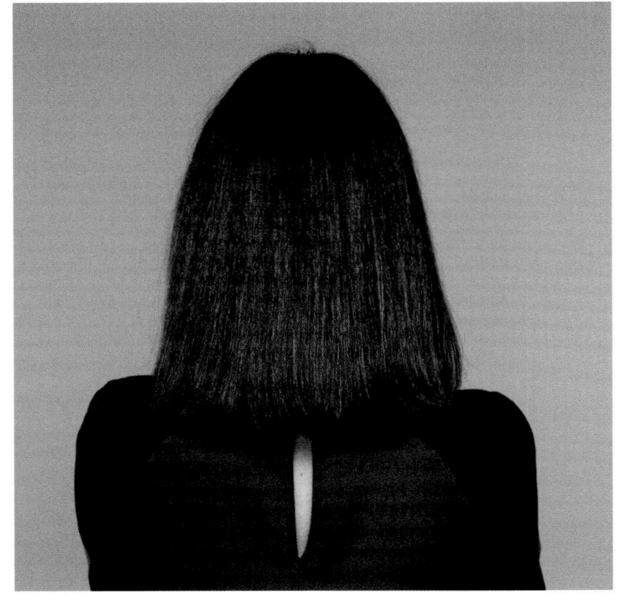

Sarah Golding

CHIEF EXECUTIVE OFFICER, THE&PARTNERSHIP UK

Pitches: they are the best of times and the worst of times. The tests of my professional resilience. The best because they bring an agency together, determined to prevail. The worst because they are high-stress events and always involve working late into the evenings and weekends, taking people away from their families for months.

As an agency, we have to balance the demands we put on our people as well as ensuring we are all primed and ready to seize every golden pitching opportunity. So we have created The & Academy, where we send all managers on a mental health first-aid course, and Well Good Fun, which are physical clubs to help our people stay fit and strong. We also have rooms which are phone and paper free, where people can escape for a quiet break. These are particularly important as our agency is a loud, buzzy, creative place.

However, as CEO I am one of the few people involved in almost every pitch, so I have to build up my own additional resilience. There's no doubt that coming from the north of England helps, because it's in our DNA to just get on with things (and no one will ever see us cry). But, even with that on my side, I need my squad around me; my wonderful leadership team who share the load, bounce ideas around and keep me constantly laughing through life.

But without doubt for me, the best thing I do to build my wellbeing is to hide at home whenever I can. My lounge, my sofa, my husband, a box set, a foot rub and a slab of very dark chocolate. It is heaven. Right at that moment nothing bad can happen, even if we have just lost a pitch.

I lounge on the sofa with my husband box sets and eating a big slab of chocolate. When I do this, nothin bad can happen.

atching
ark

I get my resilience from my family – nothing is more important than my family.

Sally Boyle

MANAGING DIRECTOR, GOLDMAN SACHS INTERNATIONAL

We can only have productive, happy, healthy employees if they feel supported from a physical and mental health perspective. Individuals need to understand the need to be resilient and firms need to know that they have an obligation to support them.

In our workplace, we focus on making sure managers really know their people and look for the signs of any mental health issues. We have done a lot of training to make sure that they are empathetic and we have talked to our employees to make sure they look after themselves with things like a good night's sleep, hydration and downtime. For our part, we provide a GP practice, psychologist and gym, all on-site.

Often, senior people don't share their personal experiences and it would be odd if they didn't have any because we know the statistics. I get my resilience from my family – nothing is more important than my family. At the end of the day I can chat to my husband or children and it helps me to get perspective. They give me energy and confidence to go in the next day.

The investment banking industry is notoriously hard-nosed, macho, highly professional, high-energy, focussed and relentless in its pursuit of growth. It is a tough environment where resilience is everything but opening up to mental health issues is still not the norm. Sally is part of the transformation of the culture at Goldman Sachs.

Dame Carolyn McCall DBE

CHIEF EXECUTIVE OFFICER, ITV | NON-EXECUTIVE BOARD, DEPARTMENT FOR BUSINESS, ENERGY AND INDUSTRIAL STRATEGY | NON-EXECUTIVE DIRECTOR, BURBERRY PLC | TRUSTEE, ROYAL ACADEMY

I think my childhood built a degree of resilience in me quite early on as I was born and brought up in India and also lived in Singapore. I was an only child and we moved for my father's job quite a lot so I had to adapt to different schools and environments from an early age. Going to boarding school developed that too. I always had a secure and loving family which underpinned my childhood. That unspoken support has been important to me in creating inner resilience.

I am naturally positive and optimistic, but I believe that everyone's resilience can be tested. Every time mine is, I feel it has been strengthened and developed.

How I viewed work changed dramatically when I got my first management role running a team at The Guardian. I remember feeling a huge sense of responsibility and that has never really left me, as you realise how much impact you have on other people's lives every day and I always wanted that to be as positive as possible.

As you become more senior, you learn that you have to think about your own way of balancing your life to ensure you are not depleting the reserves you will inevitably need for the tough moments.

The most difficult period for me in business was probably when I arrived at EasyJet, and then in 2016 after the referendum result.

In 2010 aviation was a new sector for me, I didn't know anyone in it and it is very tough and male-skewed. I was dealing with a turnaround as well as many other factors, and my resilience was tested most weeks. I tried hard to create a culture of openness and inclusion. I also took wellbeing seriously, which sometimes felt like a battle in a fast-paced, low-cost environment.

We did many good things for our people and customers including supporting our pilots and people on the frontline and working with an independent doctor who helped us better understand the issue of fatigue. We also launched the Amy Johnson Initiative aiming for 20 per cent of all new entrant pilots to be women by 2020. That will be achieved.

The role of the CEO is to absorb a lot of uncertainty and not allow it to derail people within the organisation. I do my utmost to galvanise, focus and strengthen the business to cope with the adverse headwinds and shocks.

The day after the referendum in 2016, I stood in front of everyone in the hangar in Luton and reassured them that we had a contingency plan and would implement it immediately; that they would all be able to stay in their roles, which was making half of them very anxious as they were EU citizens, and that it would be OK. It was a very difficult moment for a European airline which had been founded because of EU deregulation.

As CEO in a publicly quoted company, you are often in the public eye because you are justifying strategy or a decision that you've taken with your board. The quarterly pressure on numbers can feel relentless and doing the right things for your company long-term has to stay at the front of your mind.

Ensuring that you are pacing yourself and keeping well is critical as it helps with decision-making and energy. Always easier said than done.

A lot of CEOs I know will find their energy and resilience from having other interests. I love playing tennis, reading and seeing great art, particularly at the Royal Academy where I am a trustee. Having outside passions keeps me sane, as do my family and friends.

TOP TIP

Have other things that give you strength and positive energy. Spend time with friends who don't care about what you do for a living and just want to be with you.

Find a job where you really like what you do. It sounds obvious, but so many people say they don't like their job.

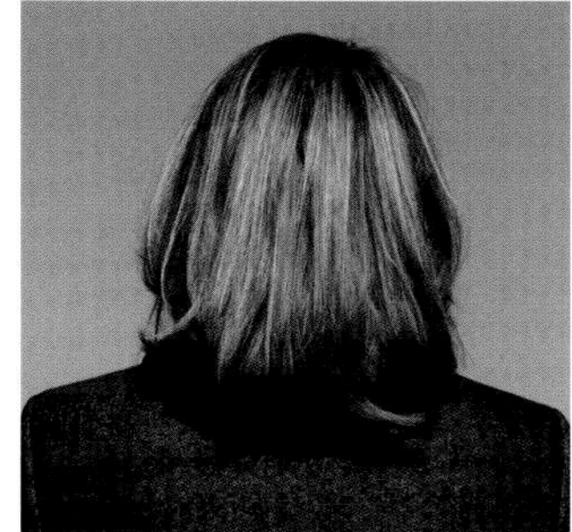

TOP TIPS

Pause and turn your back on FOMO by reimagining the workplace.

ONE
Look realistically at your business strategy, your performance measures and your ways of working. Now be prepared to change everything to create a new, more effective culture focused on the wellbeing and resilience of your people.

TWO
Get perspective. Be honest and open as leaders, talk about your concerns and be a good listener. Saying things out loud and being open can reduce stress. As leaders, be prepared to do this yourselves so that everyone else feels it is OK.

THREE
Always have integrity and humility. People want to trust and believe in their leader because they understand the business and their personal value.

FOUR
Invest in training your people in the skills of wellbeing and resilience. It will improve personal and business performance.

FIVE
Listen. Go and meet people and spend time with them. Use your emotional intelligence to understand yourself, your colleagues and your staff. There will be stuff going on that you have no idea about.

SIX
Think about the impact of real diversity and inclusion, plus flexible working policies and agile processes to find the right balance for your business.

SEVEN
Create a development board and empower the next generation of leaders to help lead the business forward.

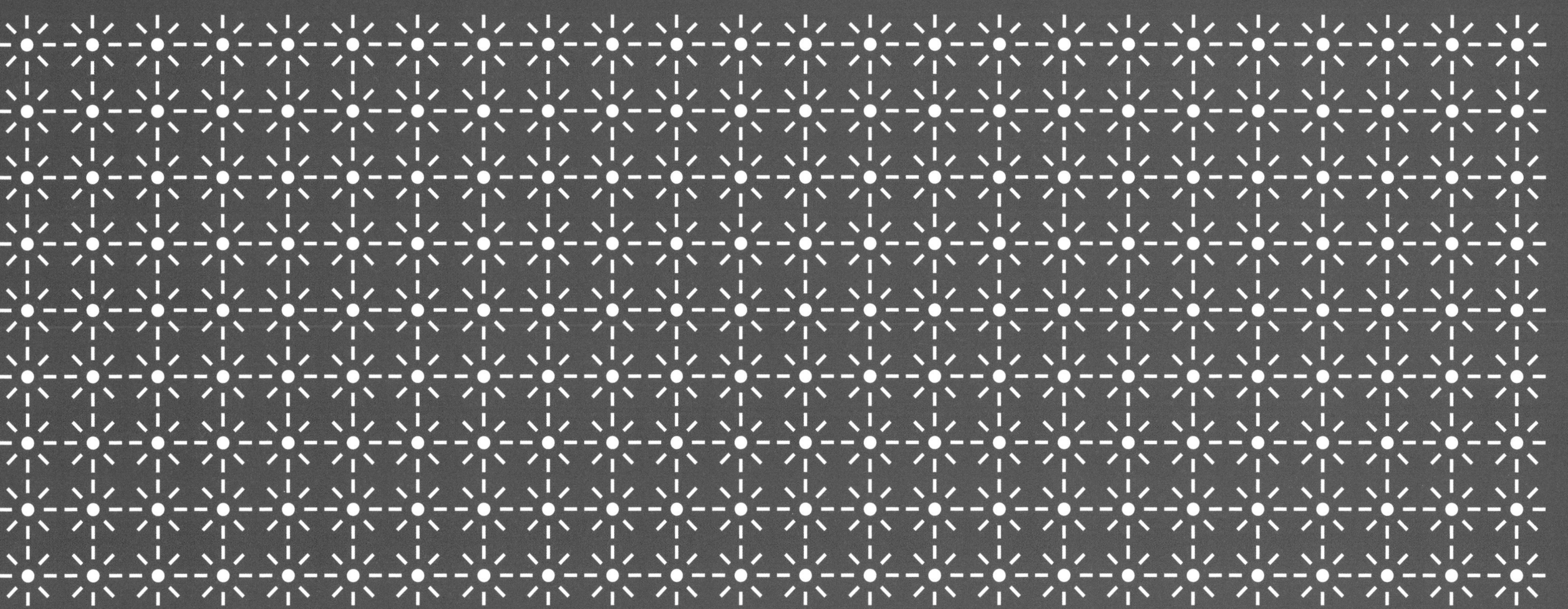

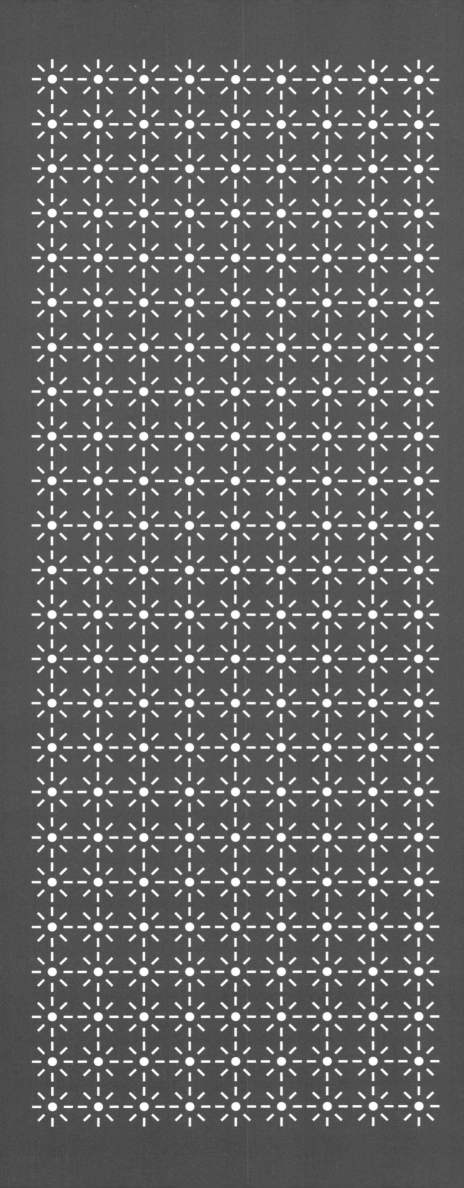

Chapter three

Entrepreneurs and the start-up story

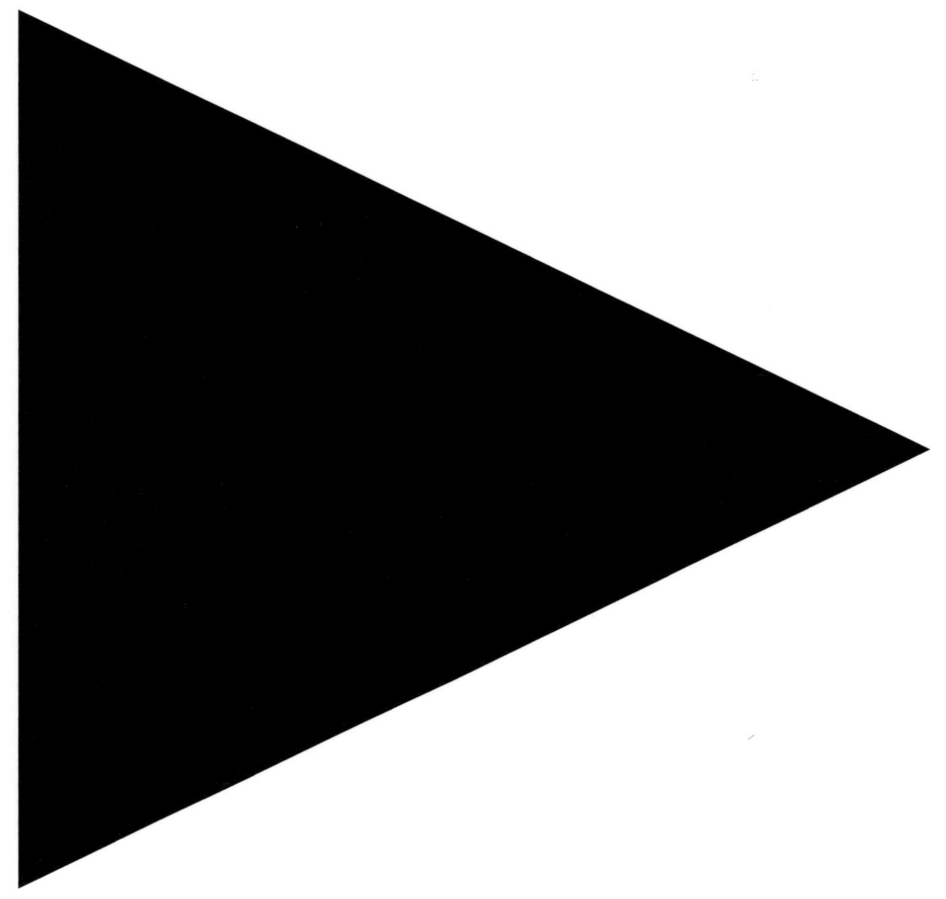

Pressing PLAY on start-up life

Let's Reset is my fourth business. The start-up phase is similar every time: exciting, stimulating, challenging, lonely, dynamic and very, very hard work. When I started my first – a gin business – almost 20 years ago (way before its time), I hadn't even heard of the word entrepreneur. Now, entrepreneurs and SME founders are celebrated as UK growth heroes.

Success is championed in magazines, on stages and across social media, fuelling a glossy, heroic image of entrepreneurship. When founders succeed, start-ups succeed and we all win. According to IW Capital, SMEs make up around 98 per cent of businesses in the UK contributing £1.9 trillion each year towards the economy.

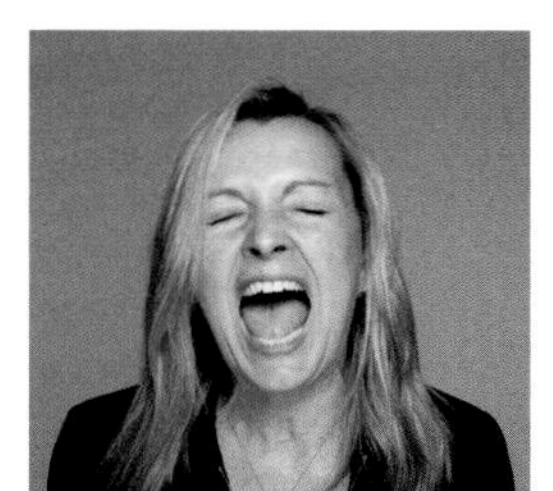

However, start-up life is complex and tough.

According to weare3Sixty's Entrepreneur Pressure and Wellbeing Study 2019, nine out of ten entrepreneurs reported signs of mental health strain, with symptoms including sleep issues, exhaustion, panic attacks and migraines. In a comparable study of those in employment, 60 per cent of employees showed signs of poor mental health due to work. The three biggest pressures are, unsurprisingly, risk, the challenge of decision-making and a lack of resources (including time). Grit or resilience is, for almost all of us, seen as vital and comes through really strongly in this next chapter.

For me, the most striking statistic was that 78 per cent of founders feel lonely on the start-up journey, which was genuinely a revelation. I really thought I was unusual in feeling this. I think it's an emotion that so many leaders experience and it can, at times, be crippling. It's often spoken about by leaders at all levels of industry, but somehow, as an entrepreneur, it feels more personal.

However, just like me, almost all entrepreneurs love what they do and are passionate to make a difference. A focus on commercial outcomes is, of course, vital, but creating and finding supportive environments plus building soft skills like wellbeing and resilience enables us to thrive as well as survive.

When I first met Rose she was hugely supportive of Let's Reset, so I am delighted that she is part of the book. Rose is a well-known actress (The Doom Generation, Scream, Charmed), activist and she is also incredibly brave (this is also the title of her book). She's a woman who continues to speak out, whose sexual assault accusation against Harvey Weinstein proved pivotal in felling the Miramax mogul and whose #RoseArmy has helped galvanise the #MeToo fight against systemic predatory misogyny within Hollywood and beyond.

Rose McGowan

ACTRESS, ACTIVIST, MODEL AND AUTHOR

One of the greatest tricks that the patriarchy plays on women is to deliberately destabilise them, then use their instability as a reason to disbelieve them. I have written my book Brave as a manifesto. It's a call to arms – not just against the specific men who mistreated me and the men and women who enabled that mistreatment, but against an industry. I was born in one cult and came of age in another, more visible cult: Hollywood.

In a strange world where I was continually on display, stardom soon became a personal nightmare of constant exposure and sexualisation. I escaped into the world of my mind, something I had done as a child, and into high-profile relationships. Every detail of my personal life became public, and the realities of an inherently sexist industry emerged with every script, role, public appearance, and magazine cover. The Hollywood machine packaged me as a sexualised bombshell, hijacking my image and identity and marketing them for profit.

Hollywood expected me to be silent and cooperative, and to stay on the path. Instead, I rebelled and asserted my true identity and voice. I re-emerged unscripted, courageous, victorious, angry, smart, fierce, unapologetic, controversial, and real as fuck. Brave is the story of how I fought my way out of these cults and reclaimed my life. I want to help everyone do the same. If we try and speak out, look after our mental health and cherish our wellbeing we can improve ourselves and our business environment by 10 per cent at a time. All of us can make a difference.

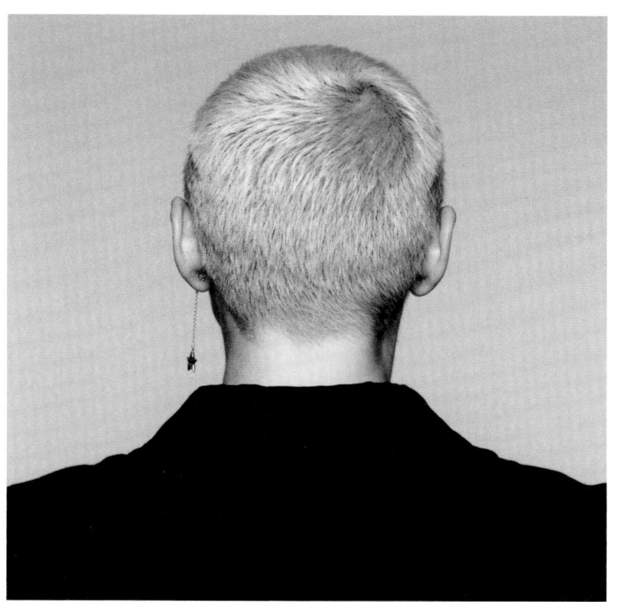

N I HAVE BIG CHALLENGES
WAYS THINK, 'WHAT WOULD
MUM DO?'

Luke Massie

FOUNDER, VIBE GROUP

When I set my business up at 20 I really doubted myself, but as a start-up founder you have to be resilient. To give it the best shot, you have to believe in yourself. You give off what you get. I believe that if you are loyal and resilient you give yourself the best chance.

There are a number of challenges I face every day. Resilience captures all those human traits and without it I will fail. In the workplace there is a lot of change, my world is fast-paced and the world is fast-paced too. I have had to spend time out of the business for 'me-time', time with loved ones and social wellbeing. I promote this internally as mental health and wellbeing are important to me.

I spend a lot of time with my direct reports trying to understand what motivates them and their personal lives. I want it to be that we would go to war together. I want them to feel listened to and we need to understand each other's pain and barriers.

Let's have this conversation again in five years. If you want to build a long-lasting legacy you need to build on strong foundations, not on quicksand. You need to invest in people and their wellbeing. Neglecting your mental health could have huge costs.

GB track and field Paralympian Stef Reid MBE is an athlete, broadcaster, and speaker. She is the reigning long jump World Champion, and a three-time Paralympic medallist in the sprint and the long jump. Stef lost her right foot in a boating accident when she was 15. She thought she had lost her dreams of being an athlete as well. But, when Stef got her first prosthetic running leg, she realized it wasn't over, it was just going to look a bit different.

It is better to marinate in an ugly emotion than artificially create a positive one. Explore uncomfortable feelings so you can deal with them and move on.

Stef Reid MBE

BRITISH PARALYMPIAN, BROADCASTER, AND SPEAKER

Resilience is important because life is hard. We need to expect that it will be hard and embrace the challenge. Performance is not just physical – your mind is as important as your body. I have to take care of my mind so that I am in a position to compete well and do my best. I have to prepare it to handle the pressure of competing in front of huge crowds, knowing that years of hard work come down to a few moments. Taking care of your mind is like cleaning your house – it is much easier to do in little chunks every week instead of letting things build up. For example, if I've had a disagreement with my husband or coach, and it is weighing on my mind, I would rather deal with it immediately and move on. I don't want to devote head space to mulling it over or being angry. When I am performing, I need all of my focus and all of my mental resources.

Journaling works really well for me. I like to keep track of things I am thinking, and things I am saying to myself. Sometimes I am surprised by my thoughts or the things I am saying to myself. Just noticing them is the first step in changing negative thought patterns. When I write down my worries, I can see them more objectively and make a plan to deal with them. Ignoring them never works. It is better to marinate in an ugly emotion than artificially create a positive one. Explore the uncomfortable feelings so you can deal with them and move on.

Sometimes I feel like my value as a person and an athlete is tied to my performance. Intellectually, I know it is not true. I like my friends regardless of how they perform at work or on the track. But it is hard not to fall into this trap when we spend so much time in the artificial world of social media, which celebrates perfection. There is no quick fix, but as I get older, I'm starting to find perfection kind of boring. I like adventure more.

James Routledge

FOUNDER, SANCTUS

I was struggling with my mental health in my 20s. I was uncertain, scared and didn't know who to turn to. I couldn't admit it to myself, but eventually, when I opened up, it transformed my relationship with work and with my friends. It was a positive experience. It's OK to admit to being vulnerable. As soon as I allowed myself to take the risk of admitting how I was feeling, people would also reciprocate, and I had a sense of connection that I had not had before.

Some people feel that they must leave their personal life at the work door. A funeral or a doctor's appointment are normal. A workplace can create an environment where people can bring their human selves to work and that must come from the top. It must be a real commitment, not just yoga sessions and bean bags.

Great businesses now want to create a more holistic and inclusive environment. It's not that people will be crying about their mental health over their lunch, but they could if they wanted to. The biggest barrier is cultural change. There is a perception that mental health is a weakness. It shows real strength to be able to talk about it.

We all have mental health. We have this antiquated view that it is only for some people and we are crazy. Yes, we are all crazy.

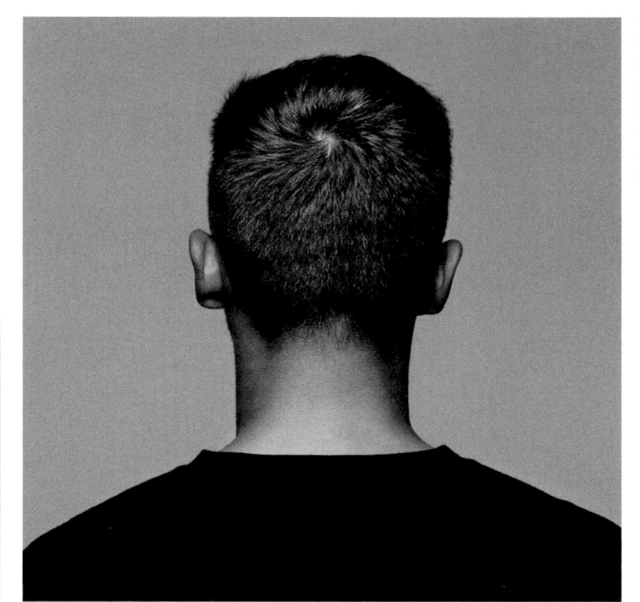

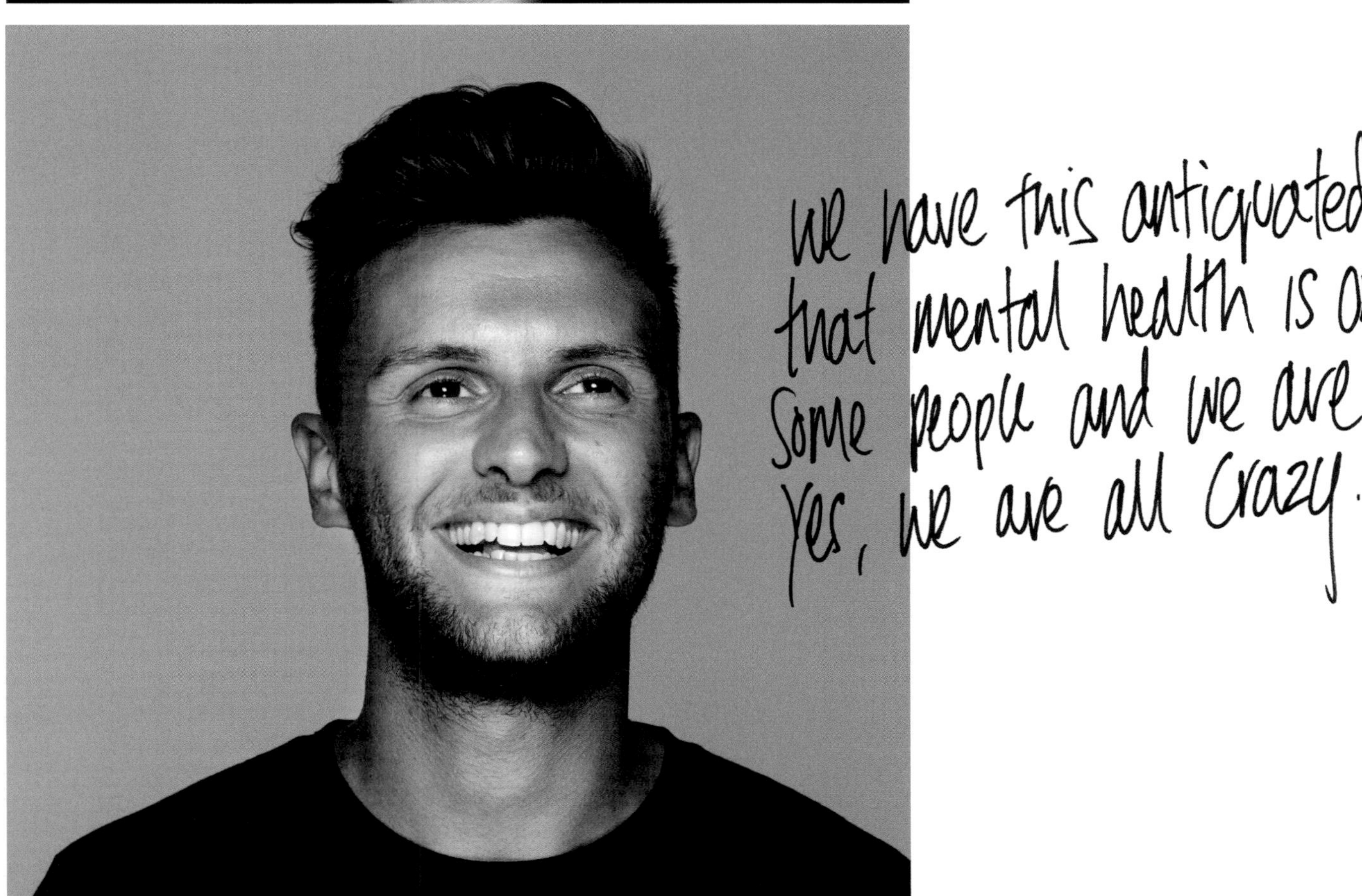

We have this antiquated view that mental health is only for some people and we are crazy. Yes, we are all crazy.

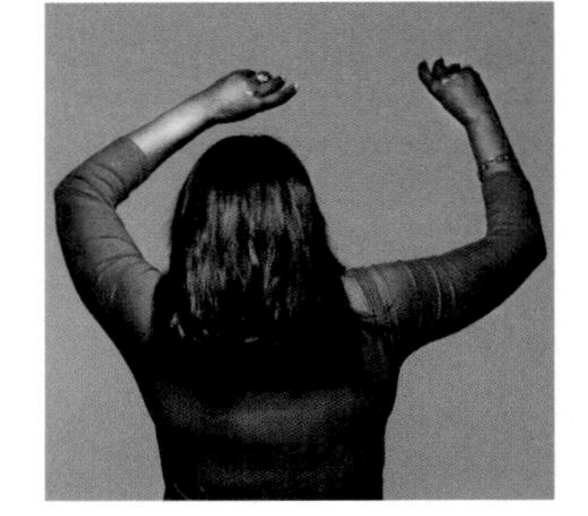

Angie Greaves

RADIO PRESENTER

Resilience and wellbeing were never things I had considered deep down. I just mirrored my mother and her generation who held it together and got on with it.

Looking back now, when my Mum was going through emotionally challenging times she brushed herself and her feelings aside to make sure everyone else was OK. She put herself at the bottom of the pile and, as a result, totally burned out.

It's such a positive step that we are now in the place to admit, 'Yes I have a great job, drive a nice car and have a nice home, but there are certain times of the day when coping with all that life throws at me is a challenge' – and at that point, those material things are irrelevant.

When I'm struggling at work, I put a couple of songs on that I know will relax me. I fix my makeup and try to find a place of calm. I don't want emotions to boil up at the wrong time, especially when I'm on air.

As long as we realise that we are humans, not robots, it is OK to let go every now and then. It's no longer embarrassing or a sign of weakness to admit, 'I can't do this anymore'. It is, in fact, a sign of strength to own up to how you truly feel.

WE HAVE NOW COME TO RECOGNISE THAT IGNORING THE NEGATIVE FEELINGS WE ARE EXPERIENCING ACTUALLY DOES US MORE HARM THAN GOOD.

TOP TIP

Be honest with yourself, sometimes just stop and think, EBBOM: Engage Brain Before Opening Mouth.

Steve Parish

CHAIRMAN, CRYSTAL PALACE FOOTBALL CLUB | FORMER FOUNDER, TAG WORLDWIDE

I come from a generation where words like 'wellbeing' and 'anxiety' were little-used and even less understood. I'm pretty resilient and have probably expected those around me to be the same, although I would like to think I'm sensitive to those among us who find some situations and setbacks tougher to deal with.

Maybe it's age, maybe it's my second and more public venture of being an owner and Chairman of a football club, but I am far more aware of situations and challenges that can contribute to great anxiety, worry and, in some cases, serious mental health issues.

This is often exacerbated by both the terrible criticism and aspirational lives found now on social media that have brought into focus the vulnerability many people, and indeed myself, feel from time to time.

I focus first on the basics like good sleep. The most important part is not to subscribe to this, 'No sleep equals success' bollocks, because for most of us it just equals being tired, miserable and operating way below maximum capacity. The other basics are fitness, health and diet. I make these things as much of a priority as I can. If you get those right and feel good about yourself in general, then everything else looks surmountable.

If one particular thing is troubling you, find an unrelated goal or activity that distracts you from it. Learn a language, run a marathon or do something that might help you grow. Every negative thing that happens in your life is something to bounce off of. The difficult days are what make the good days so good; how to act and react when things go badly defines your life not the days when things are good.

'Count your blessings' may be an old saying but, when things are difficult, try adding up all the good things in your life. From being born in a fantastic and free country (despite all our issues and imperfections we are one of the world's great societies) to your family and friends, think of anything that makes you happy.

If your problems run deeper, if you find you can't find the answers, if the things others find easy seem difficult or impossible then speak to someone. Whether it's someone close or a professional, it will help you understand that there are no answers, only methods to help you find a way to overcome the challenges in front of you.

TOP TIP

Practice making decisions, so when it's really important you know how to really make a difference.

> ou think you
> ng to die,
> becomes more
> precious.

Suki Thompson

FOUNDER, AUTHOR, CHIEF EXECUTIVE OFFICER, LET'S RESET | CHAIR, OSTERCATCHERS/XEIM | NON-EXECUTIVE DIRECTOR, GATEWAY PLC

'If you do that again', I quipped to the specialist, 'I will drown when I do my practice swim tonight for my triathlon'. 'Lie still', he told me as he stuck the needle again into my breast, the tumour is small and hard to get. I looked over at the nurse standing to my right and by the look on her face I knew I had cancer. My latest business, Oystercatchers, was only 18 months old; I was recently single, my children Jaz and Sam were eight and ten and I felt like I was drowning.

But my business partner, Peter, my clients, industry mates, family and friends leaned in and supported me and my business and I got through it, survived and thrived. My first job was to work in a surf shop in Perranporth, Cornwall for a wonderful man called John Heath. He used to stand at the shop door and welcome everyone in, patiently teaching them about surfing. He brought surfboards and skateboards to the UK that had never been seen before and looked after all of his staff. He demanded high standards and we always had to be attentive to our customers, learn about the new products, and make money. In return he gave us great rewards, like surfing in our lunch hour, beach parties when we met our targets and doughnuts to keep us going. A perfect start to working life for a 16-year-old. I have focussed on these things ever since; challenging and delighting our customers and empowering our people to be their brilliant best selves and deliver an innovative, growing, successful business.

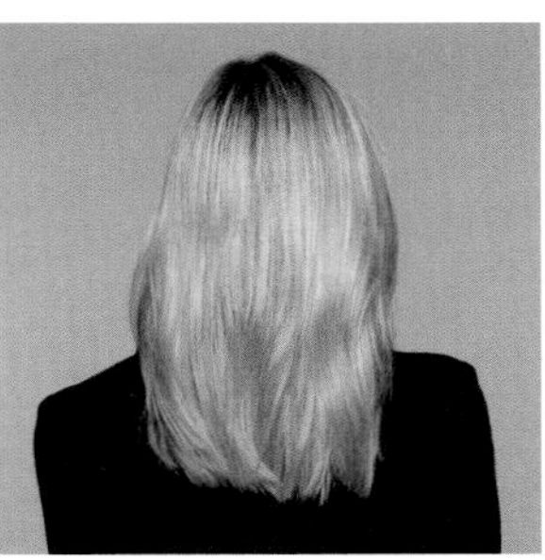

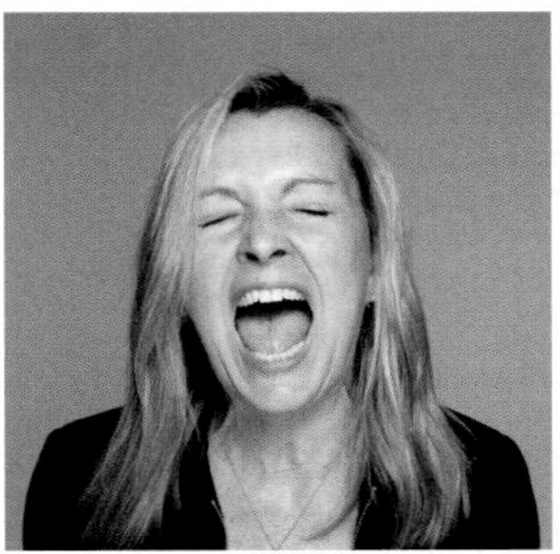

Following my treatment and second battle with cancer, I found out that I am BRCA positive, meaning I have a cancer gene and need to be closely monitored. I have full body scans every few months and have had seven operations in ten years. When you think you are going to die, living becomes precious. I still work too hard and want to cram too much into my life, but I meditate to clear my mind. I work with many clients who have become my friends and staff who inspire and challenge me. I adore my girlfriends who are always there for me, my mates who take the piss out of me, and my family who are everything to me. Some days I still feel like I'm drowning, but then I just think about what it's like surfing; I breathe and go for it all over again.

Natalie Glaze

INFLUENCER | FOUNDER, STAY WILD SWIM

It was never a career choice to be an influencer; I wanted to be a journalist so I created a blog as an online CV and it evolved from there. I blinked and then the term 'influencer' became a thing. Every week I am developing more resilience. There is a lot of pressure and there are the occasional trolls who can really affect me. I need time away from my screen so I can have 'me-time'. I put my phone on Airplane mode and I always have Sundays off.

I was my own brand and now I have an actual brand in swimwear and I need to be responsible for my customers. My brand is about sustainability, it is the core skeleton of our brand. We have tried to make every part of the process good for everyone and everything.

I put my phone on
Airplane mode and
I always have Sundays
off.

Lord Matthew J. Scheckner

GLOBAL CHIEF EXECUTIVE OFFICER, STILLWELL

I think somewhere along the line you learn to take a punch. There's a great song I love, called 'Pick Yourself Up and Start All Over Again', and sometimes, more than once in a day, that's what you have to do. I think that a very big part of my job is injecting enthusiasm into others. A very big part of what Advertising Week does, not just here in London, but all over the world, is to make people feel good about the business they're in. I feel like part of my job is being manager of a football club. That can be tough because I'm not particularly allowed to have an off day, I always have to be on my game.

I grew up an only child, and 20 years ago I found out I'm actually one of five. I found four full blood siblings at 35. But if you grow up an only child it's not like instant coffee, you don't suddenly become something else, but I'm getting used to it. I'm very used to spending time alone, and I'm very comfortable spending time alone. However, I think it's a double-edged sword spending too much time in your own head. So, over the years, I've sort of trained myself to know what's coming and to pick myself up.

At Advertising Week, we believe in our culture and our purpose. We leverage our platform to talk about issues within advertising, but also issues that transcend our industry. Whether that's sustainability within our environment, the opioid crisis, or anxiety in childhood. We also create a culture where we treat people really well. It's always family first – if someone has an issue or needs some time, they get it. My door's always open. We try and make sure everyone has a good time, so we want to give people experiences, especially at a young age, that they will cherish and learn from.

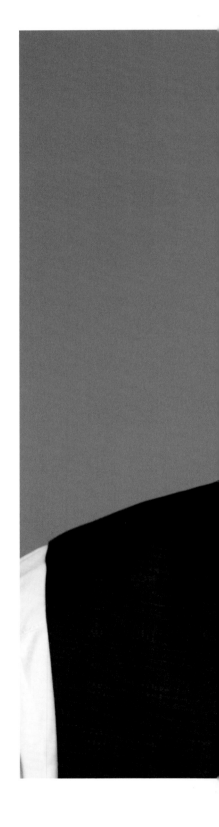

Pick yourself up and Start all over again.

AWE, Advertising Week is an international event for marketing, brand, advertising and technology professionals. Now in six major cities across the globe – New York, London, Tokyo, Mexico City, Sydney and Johannesburg. I love Matt's desire to help the broader industry and discuss issues that impact many of us beyond our everyday working lives.

TOP TIP

Focus on the key things you can do something about and less on what you can't. To get clarity of mind I try to remove myself and get outside and walk round the block for two, five or however many minutes I can. Fresh air and sky is a great place for sorting the mind.

We've just saved your life,
now go and live it.

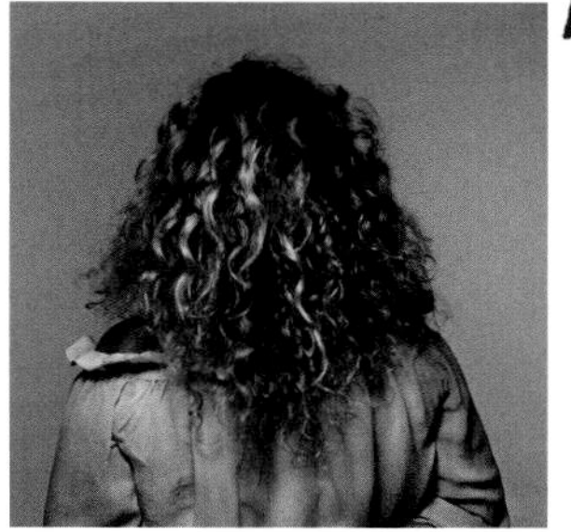

Alison van der Lande

OWNER, ALISON VAN DER LANDE HANDBAGS

Five years ago, I had a mini-stroke and then three years ago I had breast cancer. One of the doctors said to me, 'We've just saved your life, now go and live it'.

I have brought up my three children while running my business, but last year I started to feel I was cracking a bit and I hadn't focussed on my recovery enough.

In the privacy of my own home, I was very tired and had lost the excitement of it all. I have always loved travel and adventure, so I took a drastic step and I joined my daughter on her backpacking trip around South America. I left Heathrow sobbing as I didn't think I could do it, but I really wanted to be there with my daughter and live my life again. It was totally different to anything I had ever done before. We stayed in mixed hostels and I had to carry my own backpack. Things were simple; no makeup, no hair dryers, just learning to appreciate small things again and not worry about what I was always going to do. It was the turning point for me. It gave me the confidence to do the things I thought I couldn't do. Most important of all, I learned how to just stop. Last Saturday I just sat in the garden and read. I didn't weed or mow the lawn, I just read.

In a busy work environment, sometimes you just need five minutes walking around the block; thinking, processing, talking through who you are and what you are about. In my business, if people need a moment they take it. People wear a mask, but I think it is OK to show vulnerability, show some empathy and allow people some space to do it. My life was saved for a reason, twice. Now I intend to live it.

Anthony Vivian Thompson

THOMPSON'S SCHOOL OF MOTORING, THE DRIVING FORCE OF SOUTH LONDON

As you age, your perspective and your ability to manage stress evolves. Over 40 years ago my mates and I formed what was the first black punk band called Basement 5, signed to Island Records. Angie Bowie, Chrissie Hynde, David Bowie and Johnny Rotten were no strangers to the flat that we shared during that time. We gigged like there was no tomorrow at many iconic venues across London and enjoyed the relative stardom that followed. Eventually, stress and depression reared their ugly heads within the group and the dynamics of the band were affected forever.

Today, my brother and I run our own driving school. You'd be wrong if you felt my now chosen career was free of stress. I now live my life in chunks of an hour at a time. 10am to 11am, Brother Emmanuel; 11am to 12 noon, Mrs Johnson and so on. I have learned that the only way for me to deal with the workload is to adapt my personality by the hour, one hour at a time. Each of my customers have different needs, unique to them, behind the wheel. As their instructor, I must accommodate that to give them the best learner driving experience possible. You might not imagine it, but at the end of the day, I'm spent, heavy with all the personalities I've had to take on that day. When I get home, solitude for an hour or so normally does the trick to uncouple me from the toil of the day. If Arsenal are doing well, even better. A night-time stroll to complete the de-stress, a good night's sleep and my engines are revving for Mrs Jones at 09.30. I've recharged, rebooted and reset.

'Keep calm and carry on' is detrimental to people's wellbeing'

Jess Sharp

MENTAL HEALTH INFLUENCER

I believe you just need to be honest. There is no point in trying to power through. I hate the phrase, 'Man up'. If you are sad, you are sad. I wish more people would go and talk to others. When people know what's going on, they can offer support. 'Keep calm and carry on' is detrimental to people's wellbeing. We need to acknowledge when we are having a hard time – it is never forever. We need to acknowledge and feel it when it happens.

If you had a gaping wound, you would be told to go home, but people put on a brave face and power on with mental health issues. If you are on uneven ground people will help you. In the workplace people are first-aid trained but there is also mental first aid and more companies need to invest in this. It is so important that we all learn to recognise the signs to look out for and the impact that challenges both in and out of work have on people.

I started therapy because I was in a job that didn't support mental health. I would doodle the messages my therapist gave me and put them on Instagram where they resonated with people and I gained a following. They help others, but they are also a reminder to me.

I put the messages from my Insta account on to greetings cards. I discovered there was a gap in the market for them. Messages like, 'It will pass' and, 'People are struggling all the time'. I am told the cards I design verbalise what people want to say. I hope they give them the strength to carry on.

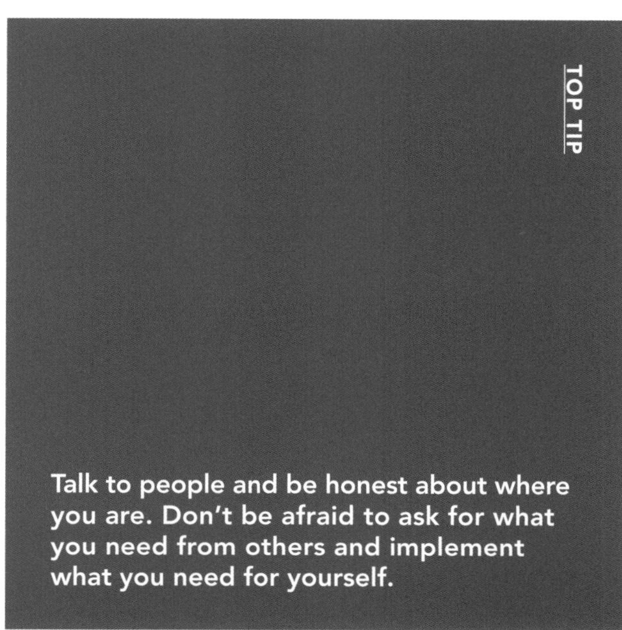

TOP TIP
Talk to people and be honest about where you are. Don't be afraid to ask for what you need from others and implement what you need for yourself.

Tim Moore

TRAVEL AUTHOR
TITLES INCLUDE: THE CYCLIST WHO WENT OUT IN THE COLD, FRENCH REVOLUTIONS AND NUL POINTS

I have written 11 travel books about very adventurous things, but I am ill-equipped to do them. Because I am such an unadventurous person, my routine is that I sit in front of the computer in my dressing gown, pretending to work for two years, and then I must atone for it, so I embark on these mad adventures.

The scariest thing I have ever done (and I get scared easily), where I thought, 'Shit this is really, really bad', was when I decided to ride a bike along the length of the Iron Curtain. I thought it would be funny to do it on an old communist era shopping bike with no gears and small wheels. And then I thought I would make it interesting by cycling during winter. It was without doubt the most stupid thing I have ever done. As soon as I started, there was a blizzard and it was minus 20 degrees.

There were times when it was so cold I could hardly move. I didn't know where I was, there was no phone signal and it was 70 miles to the nearest house, let alone town. It was testament to human kindness that the local Finns would warn the people in the towns along the route that I was heading their way and they would welcome me. It was 6,000 miles and I couldn't believe how long it took. I was in complete despair as I thought I would never finish it. But I said I would do it and I couldn't give up, so I just took one day at a time. I would think about it in little blocks, not the big picture. If I could just get to the next petrol station (and there are a lot in Finland) and get a microwaveable burger I would be OK.

My books are supposed to be funny and I have undertaken expeditions that literally could have killed me. I am a middle-aged, unfit guy who is a bit feeble. If I can do it then anyone can.

I don't bottle up emotions. I still blubber like a pathetic loser to my wife on the phone when I'm feeling desperate and she gets worried, then eventually comes out to see me.

DON'T BOTTLE UP EMOTIONS. I STILL BLUBBER LIKE A PATHETIC LOSER TO MY WIFE ON THE PHONE.

Tim got fired from his office job as a computer games critic for writing surreal gibberish into his reviews. Now he works for himself, but rather than having a more relaxing life he has pushed his resilience to the extremes and escaped near death.

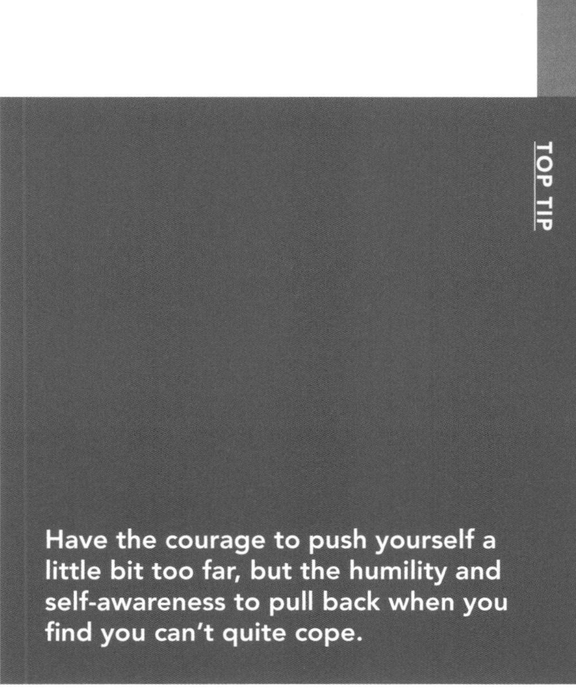

TOP TIP

Have the courage to push yourself a little bit too far, but the humility and self-awareness to pull back when you find you can't quite cope.

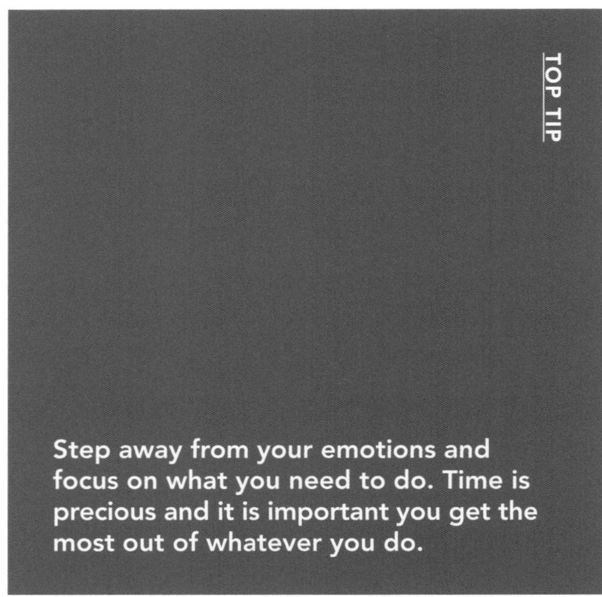

TOP TIP

Step away from your emotions and focus on what you need to do. Time is precious and it is important you get the most out of whatever you do.

The very act of smiling helped to change my inner mood and it was empowering not only to me, but to those around me.

Kim Crawford

FOUNDING PARTNER, THE JOINERY

Life was going all to plan, then suddenly my husband was diagnosed with bowel cancer. I was the breadwinner and he looked after our four children. Initially we were led to believe he would survive, so we decided to sell up and relocate to Devon, but on the day we were meant to exchange we got the news that it was terminal.

I had to run a business, provide for my family and try and keep my children's lives as normal as possible with the backdrop that my life was unravelling and my soul mate would soon be leaving us. I had to keep working as the business relied on me and my family relied on the income. Subconsciously, I started to divide my work life from home life so that I could be the best I could be in both situations just to get through. My tactic was to focus on being very present in whichever life I was in. However, I felt it was equally important to be natural and my true self. It wasn't a mask, but I had to focus on where I was and the situation in hand. I tried to keep upbeat and put a smile on. The very act of smiling helped to change my inner mood and it was empowering not only to me, but to those around me.

Serendipitously, a horse arrived in my life right in the middle of all of this. She became my therapist. I would go riding with my daughter regularly and that time with her outdoors helped me to see things more clearly and to cope better with the next challenge that would inevitably follow.

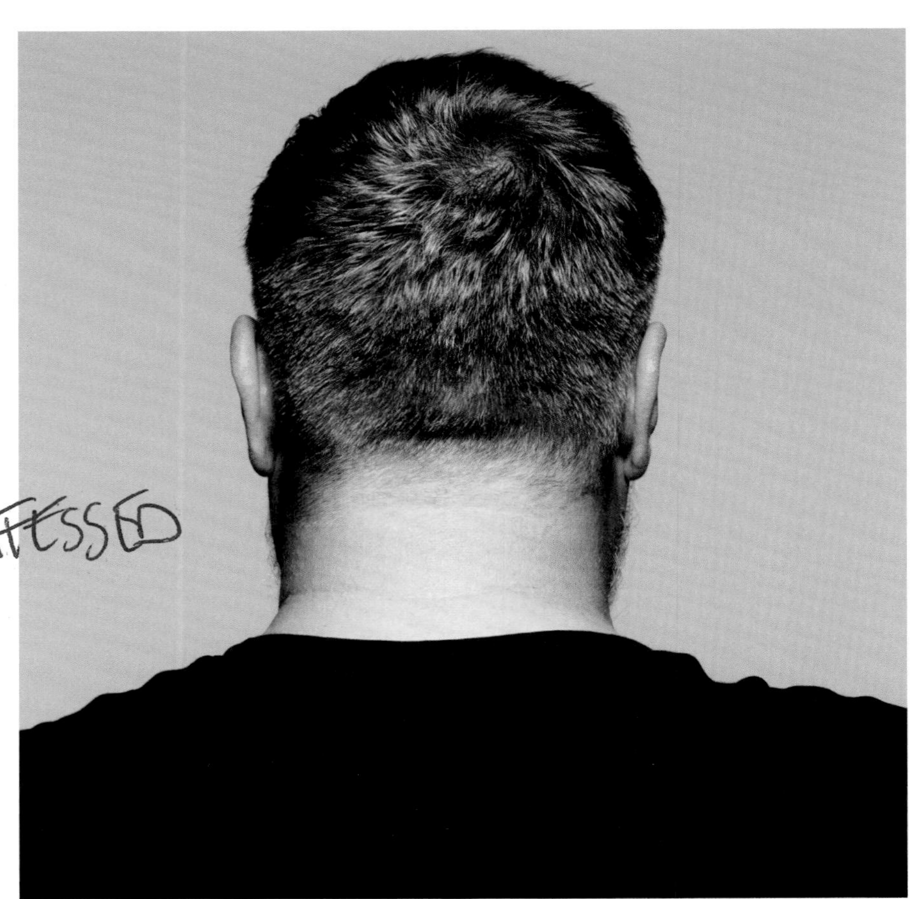

MY NAME IS RANKIN
AND I AM A SELF-CONFESSED
WORKAHOLIC.

Rankin

PHOTOGRAPHER, DIRECTOR, PUBLISHER AND CULTURAL PROVOCATEUR

FOMO has kind of snuck up on us. It's the fear that has crept into our lives through all of those new and easy to use technologies. The things that make everything simpler and have revolutionised the way we live. The things we now just take for granted. Those little mirrored things we find in our pockets control much more than we give them credit for. This shift is as big as the invention of the printing press or the industrial revolution. It's impacting our mental wellbeing in a way we could never have imagined. You see, the thing I want to promote is the concept of JOMO – the joy of missing out. Not FOMO.

The idea of addiction to technology isn't something we are entirely prepared to accept. We are still a little enamoured by the constant access to entertainment, culture, games, friends, etc. Who would give up this portable window into the lives of our heroes, frenemies and even their pet dogs?

What I realised about five years ago, is that I was seriously addicted to picking up my phone. Checking it again and again day in, day out. Why was I checking it? To stop myself from missing out. Like most addictions, it was tough to accept. A man of my age, who had never been addicted to anything (apart from work), had become hooked and fixated on always knowing what was going on. I couldn't help myself from checking. I feared not knowing.

I also realised that I wasn't just imparting this on my own consciousness, but on the 50 or so people who worked for me at the time. My initial thought was, 'Shit, I have to try to stop this'. I tried to respect not only my time, but the time off of others as well, but you know what? It's difficult. These technologies have been designed to keep you addicted, not to ease you off.

Initially, I started by drafting emails instead of always pressing send. A way to give people (and myself) a bit of breathing space. That was difficult for me – as I said, I'm a workaholic. Then I realised that was the problem. You see, workaholics were heralded in the past. We were committed and had a strong work ethic. But, back then, it was easier to have those days off because we weren't so constantly connected. Unfortunately, that ethos has hung around, long past its sell-by date. Just look at the debate around lazy millennials; what a load of bollocks.

We have to accept how the world has changed, completely, right under our noses. We cannot (and should not) look at this world through yesterday's lens (or vice versa for that matter). We need a different type of resilience. We are now connected 24/7. Even as I write this, I'm walking my dogs and dictating to myself.

Ideas come from having time to think. In the past, we had boredom forced upon us and that boredom allowed us to reset ourselves naturally. That boredom is the bedrock of creativity. I've never seen a good idea come from searching online. A clean piece of white paper, with nothing on it and just a pencil in your hand is like your brain, ready to begin. The constant connection to the rest of the world is going to be a distraction. Turn off the connection and turn on your brain. That can mean going for a walk, spending time in nature or even just lying on your bed.

Thinking, dawdling and daydreaming is underrated and underused. So, for my part in this book, I'm going to recommend that we all reset our brains. In doing this, we open up our imagination to infinite possibilities. Much more so than anything you'll find online.

So here I am, the self-confessed workaholic. My name is Rankin and I want you (and me) to get off the phone, close down the laptop and disconnect. Because we all need time to reset.

Christina Richardson

CO-FOUNDER, WEARE3SIXTY

I have been an entrepreneur since I was 18. I had some peaks and troughs of successes and failures and along the way I had a burnout and had to rewire my brain. I would get panic attacks and heart palpitations doing everyday things like walking the dog – nothing seemed to particularly trigger them. It was like a force 10 catastrophe. I had a theory that I was not the only entrepreneur experiencing high-level stress, so I interviewed a number of them and found that a staggering 90 per cent had experienced mental health issues. It made me conclude that we all need to invest in ourselves and take time to breathe.

The only way I knew was to bring my breathing back. It was a proactive thing I started every day to get myself back into the calm state. It was a long, hard slog but I can happily say I haven't had a panic attack for a year. At the back of my mind though, there is an element of fear that I could relapse. I want to be sustainable for the future and not relapse and it's not easy controlling and managing that type of situation.

I think we need to dissect human performance and learn how to deal with our emotions, identifying them and getting hold of them. I like to say, 'You have to name it to tame it'. It is a brilliant philosophy which allows me to work with it and it gives me an inner power. It is a key part of my own recovery.

When I first worked in London, I drove to work listening to Russ on Capital Radio. He was the Flying Eye, guiding me through the traffic from a helicopter, years before we could even imagine Google Maps. I had no idea of the emotional turmoil he was going through.

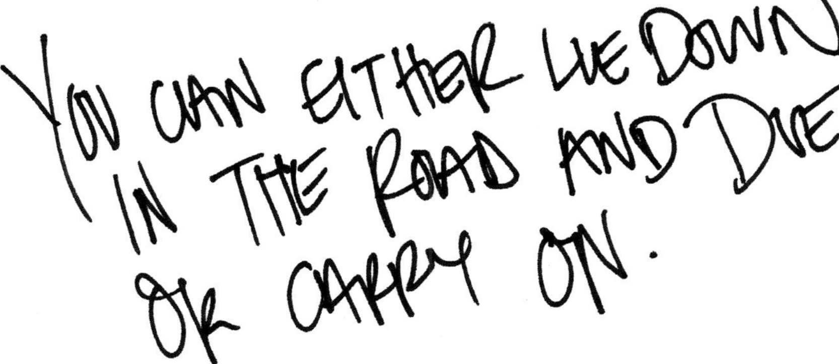

Russ Kane

AUTHOR | RADIO STATION OWNER FOR MENTAL HEALTH | COMEDIAN

When my twin boys were five their mother died. It was daunting but the train had to keep rolling and I had to put food on the table. It was then that it became very clear that people are only sympathetic for a while in business. I threw myself into my work and, weirdly, I won the most industry awards when I was at my most depressed. You can either lie down in the road and die or carry on. It's not 'one size fits all'. In most places, HR are only interested in the bottom line. In my experience, some are good but most aren't. With any trauma you go through different stages, feeling upset, then depressed, right through to anger. 'Anger is an energy', as the Public Image Ltd song told us. When I was at that anger stage, I decided to turn it into something positive.

Radio is a conversation and I love it. When I was the Flying Eye, four million people were listening to me. If I thought about that number it would have driven me nuts. Now I have my own radio stations, Men's Radio Station and Women's Radio Station, and they both have a total focus on mental health and wellbeing; there is no music or idle chit chat. It is my passion because it is not dealt with and men in particular just don't talk. Suicide statistics are 80 per cent men and 20 per cent women and it's the biggest killer of men under 40. Women are better at dealing with emotions because they talk about them. Men bottle them up and this can ultimately lead to them taking their own lives, it's truly heartbreaking. Our radio stations are a non-judgmental place where people can talk openly to experts who can help them.

I relax when I am walking the dog. I can think about my radio show, rehearse my stand up or plot out my next novel, all of which is a form of relaxation for me. I think the most important thing is to enjoy the little things in life. Tiny little things can make you disproportionately happy, like buying a book, enjoying a good cup of coffee or chatting with a pal.

I lost everything in the war!

Yulia Stark

FOUNDER, FAB ACADEMY

I remember looking at my office and the building was just burning. Everything that I had been working towards for the last three years had disappeared, all the money I had earned had literally gone up in flames. I saw people dying, it was simply horrible. I felt stuck in a horror movie. I couldn't comprehend it, I was devastated. I had worked so hard, but for what?

I remember wondering, 'Why did I actually become an entrepreneur?' The reason I had always told myself was freedom; freedom to work when I wanted and to spend time with my family. But in reality, I was working 18-hour days and I missed out on my baby boy Tristan's first steps. I said at the time to my husband, 'Give me another year, and we'll have more time'. I said to Tristan, 'Give me six months and we'll go to Disneyland' and it was all for nothing. I got stuck in the rat race. I was postponing my life for material reasons and before I knew it time had flown by and then everything was gone.

When the bombing happened, I had to slow down and I reflected on what I actually did. Did I make a difference to anyone's life? No, I didn't. All I did was import/export, I was only working for one client, and because I was working on his agenda, I was never free. So in 2014 I moved back to Belgium with my family and I said to my husband, 'Darling, from now on, whatever I do, it will contribute to society, and especially to women who want to have it all', because my Mum told me when I was little, 'You can have it all'. So I started Fab Academy with the mission that my Mum had told me about, to allow women to have it all. Of course, I can't have everything, none of us can, but now I don't put material gain in front of moments and experiences.

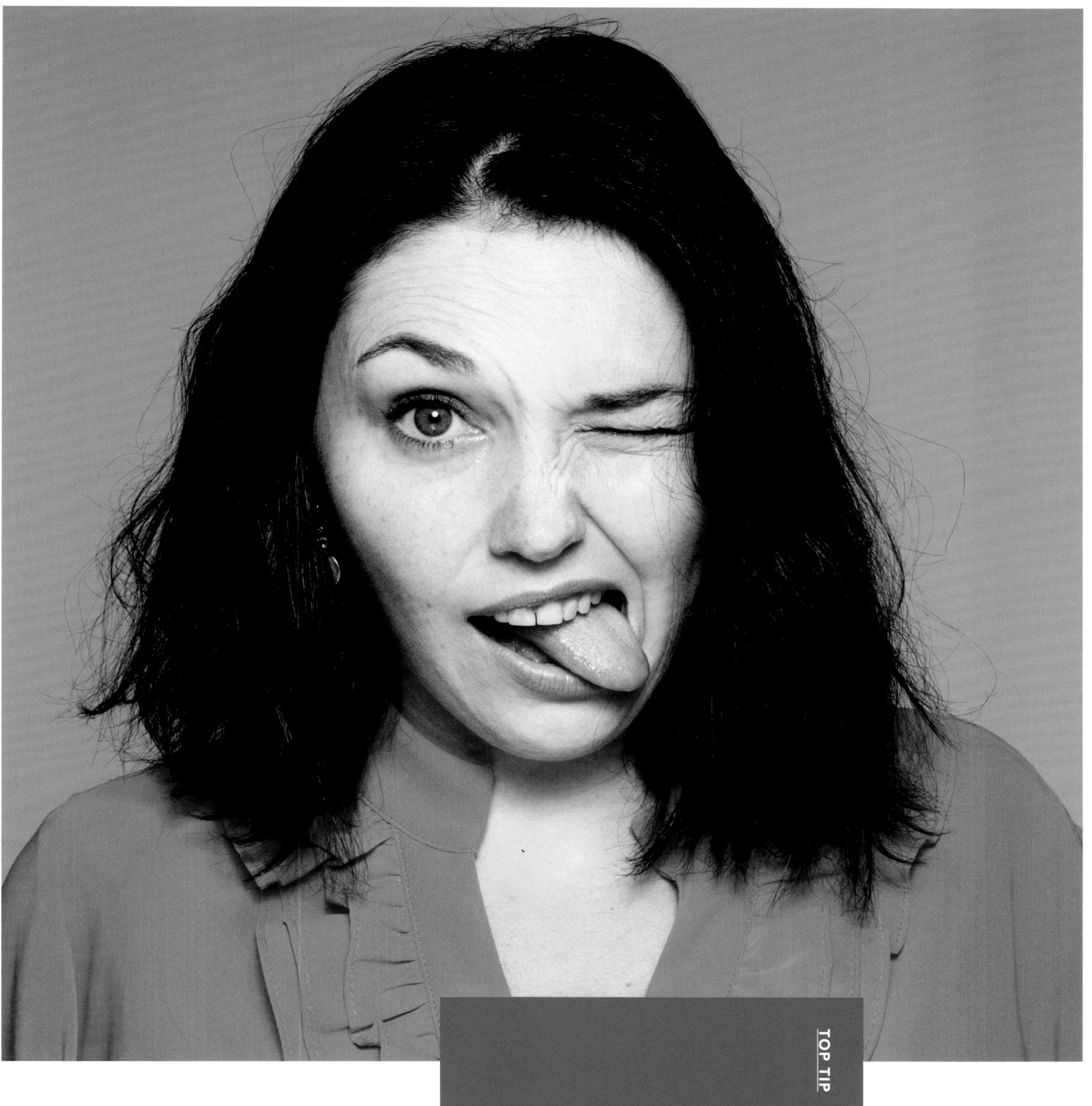

TOP TIP

Mindfulness.

Most of us are disconnected from our own core values. The moment you become more mindful your choices become more conscious, you're not a victim of circumstances, and 80 per cent of problems get solved by themselves. So don't get lost in the drama, prioritise and then work hard to stick to that.

If you have to explain to a five-year-old what you did that day, you realise that it's not that important.

Brainlabs is in The Sunday Times Small Business Top 100 Best Places to Work and it's not surprising, because Dan has put the wellbeing of his staff at the centre of his tech business as he has built it.

Daniel Gilbert

FOUNDER AND CHIEF EXECUTIVE OFFICER, BRAINLABS

My business has been a fast growth story over six years. I started in my parents' attic and now we have 300 people. When I think about business success I think about resilience first, it is not a linear path. It is about how people respond to challenges and their ability to have a positive spin on things. I believe core behaviours can be learned but when we recruit, we look for how people have responded to previous challenges. To one person a challenge could be very difficult or distressing, but to another it could be an opportunity to build and develop themselves. The difference in perspectives tells us how an individual might work within our business. We want to continue growing fast and we all need resilience to do this. Not everyone has been resilient enough to survive our journey. We want to bring in brilliant people and help them to develop and grow at a faster rate than they would elsewhere.

I have four children under five and that is the ultimate de-stress. If you have to explain to a five-year-old what you did that day you realise that it's not that important. Things can only be stressful if you label them as such. The most amazing way to contextualise things is by saying, 'I am in this situation, but what will I think of it in ten years' time?' I will probably laugh about it then, so, if that is the case, then I should really laugh about it now and forget about it. It helps to remind me how to be resilient.

TOP TIP

Understand what you can and can't control.

You may not be able to control certain situations, but you can control how you respond to them. In choosing how to respond to a given situation you will develop the sense that you can take on any challenge.

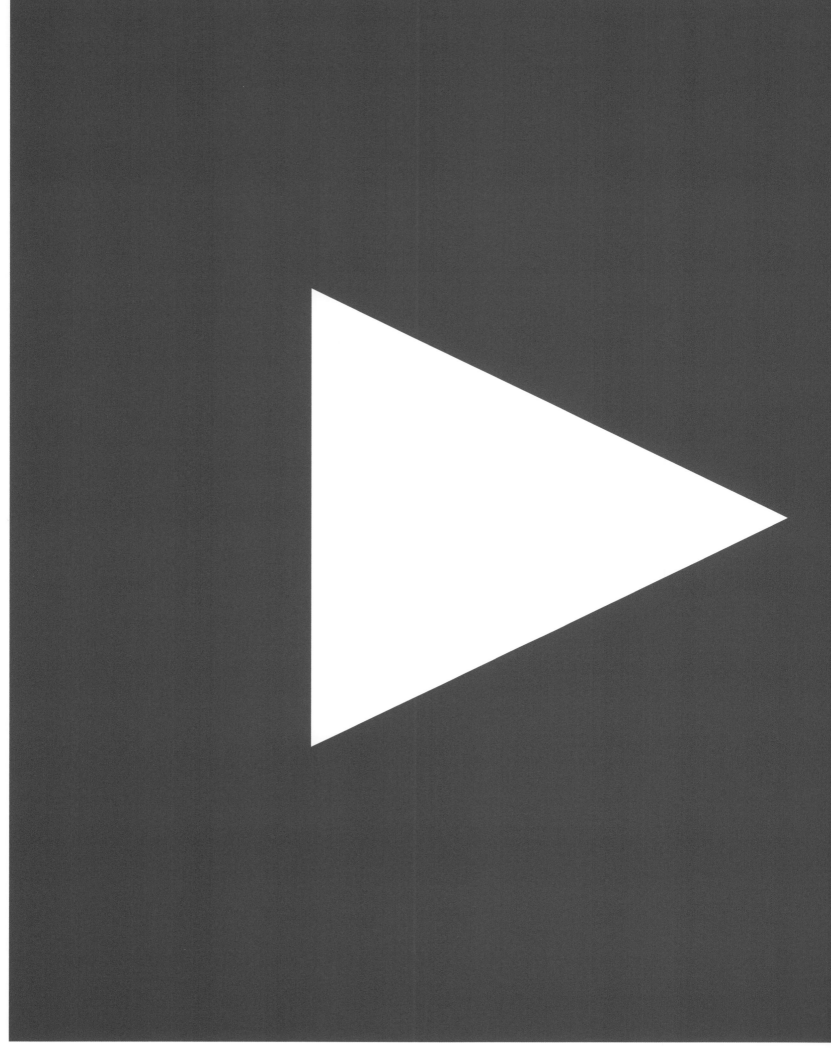

TOP TIPS

Go and do something else, take time to balance your work and home life.

ONE
Make sure you have a balance in your life between work, family and friends. Often they will overlap but try not to let your work always take the front line.

TWO
Understand what you can and can't control. You may not be able to control certain situations, but you can control how you respond to it.

THREE
Talk to people and be honest about where you are. Don't be afraid to ask for what you need from others and implement what you need for yourself.

FOUR
You learn the most about yourself when you are under pressure. It will pass, but take the learnings and, next time, do it slightly differently.

FIVE
You are the number one asset and you deserve investment just like any other business asset. Invest in personal development of skills to get the best out of yourself and your team like leaders in larger corporations do.

SIX
Nurture your support network. It's easy to lose track of accumulated stress when you're in the thick of it, so build a support network of trusted peers, professionals and friends who can help keep an eye out for the signs and work through the challenges when needed.

SEVEN
Know your goals. Each week, decide on your three big goals; share them, schedule time for them and deprioritise everything else to lessen the workload.

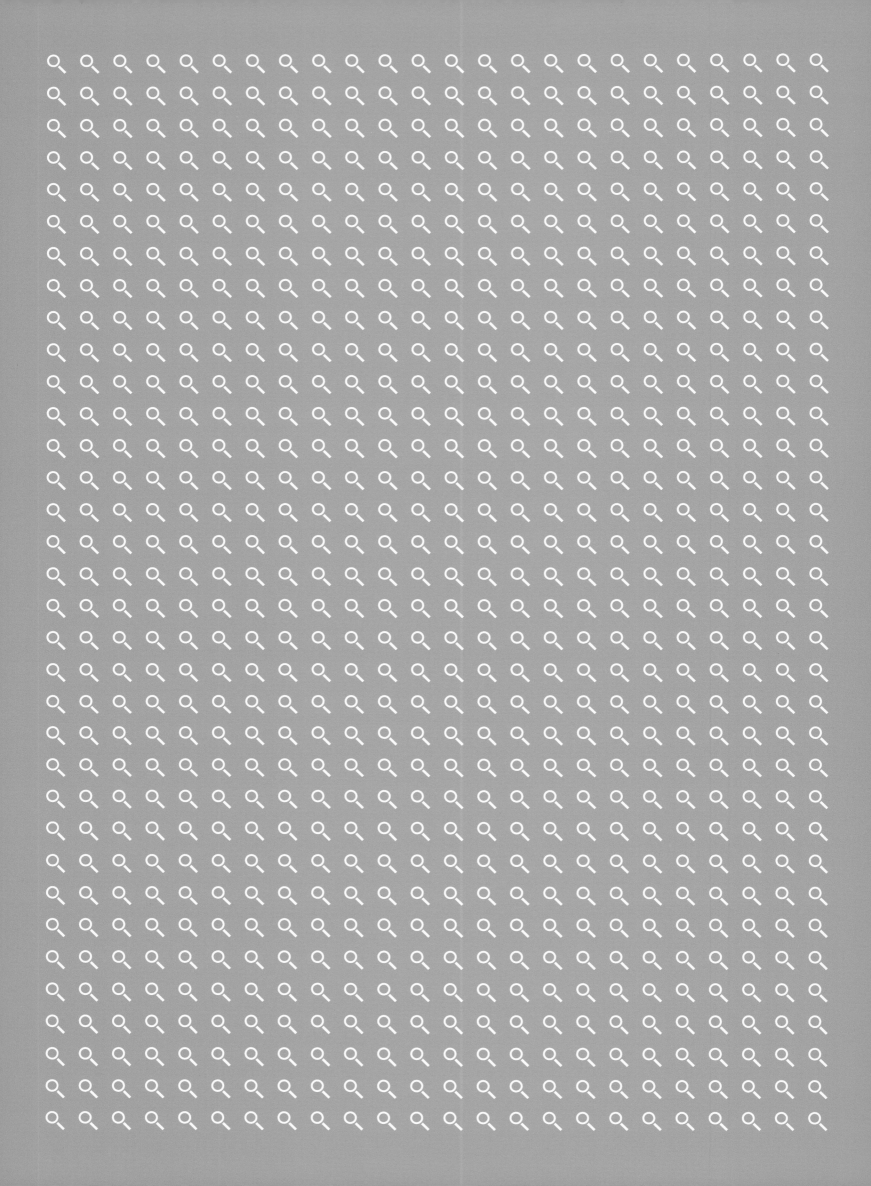

Chapter four

Experts with a different approach

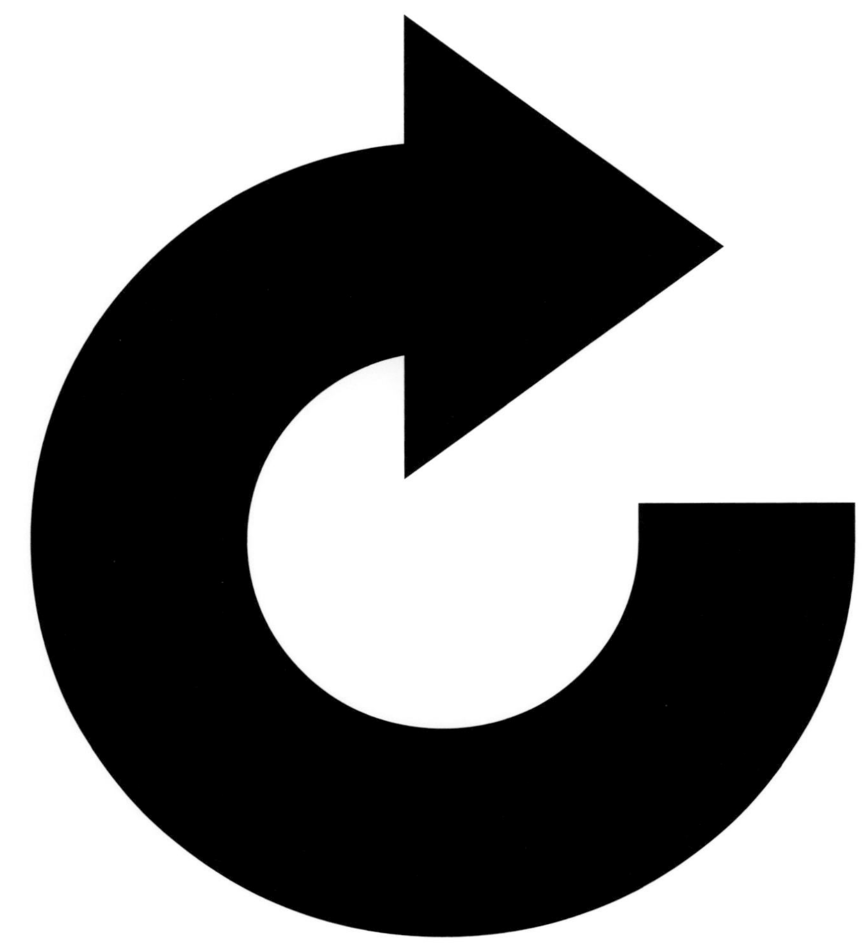

RESET yourself and your workplace

I have met wonderful experts and organisations that are working in the wellbeing space. They have their own perspectives on what we can do differently and what motivates their own wellbeing and resilience. We are privileged at Let's Reset to help companies and universities explore, experiment and embed this for themselves, all based on the latest psychological research, business approaches, cultural and behaviour change made simple and practical to apply. It is a challenging time; businesses are under pressure to create growth and financial performance. The desire for real diversity and inclusion has grown significantly, supported by high-profile initiatives such as gender pay gap reporting. Flexible working programmes are being trialled, agile ways of working being introduced, and open plan offices becoming the norm. Our whole workplace is being re-imagined which gives us the opportunity to reset our whole way of working.

The core of every great new culture is behaviour change. With the right education, skills, motivation, tools, and social support, people can change their behaviour. In my experience, wellbeing programmes are good at helping people adopt and maintain healthy behaviours, but it has to be embedded into the brand and workplace vision, ways of working, technology and measurement. Healthy behaviours lead to lower health risks and lower health risks lead to less chronic disease. With less chronic disease, employees have fewer health care costs and are happier and more effective. These are the biggest benefits of a programme at work.

In this chapter we provide insights from a variety of experts across the wellbeing and mental health industries, who share their personal advice and experience, to help us think about our wellbeing and resilience differently. Some of the profits raised from this book are being given to Mind. In 2017 the prime minister commissioned an independent review into mental health and employment led by Lord Dennis Stevenson and Mind CEO Paul Farmer. The review, Thriving at Work, was supported by an independent study on the cost to employers of the mental health problems of staff which was carried out by Deloitte. This found that poor mental health costs the UK economy as a whole over £74 billion per year.

Further research from Mind shows that 52 per cent of us experience mental health problems at work but only half of us feel comfortable to disclose this. Despite this cost, both financial and human, only 1 in 4 organisations claim to monitor staff wellbeing and mental health industry. Which to me seems crazy.

If you want to know more about any of these experts or see some of the thinking behind their approaches, you can find out more on our platform **letsreset.com**

TOP TIP

In my life, I've constantly been trying to prove myself to others, but now I've realised that I'm content with what I have because I'm happy in myself.

In our country people think that having a mental health problem means having the evil eye.

HH Sayyida Basma Bint Fakhri Al Said of Oman

FOUNDER AND MENTAL HEALTH CONSULTANT, WHISPERS OF SERENITY CLINIC

For some people in Oman when you say, 'Mental health', they think it suggests that the person is crazy. They say that they have the 'evil eye'. It is easier to talk like that as it means it's out of their hands. For me, it has been a huge challenge even to get people to accept that mental health is an issue that needs to be discussed and talked about. I set up the Whispers of Serenity Clinic in 2014. It's more than just a mental health wellness clinic. We take a holistic approach to mental wellbeing. We believe that peace of mind comes from mental and physical wellbeing and they are one and the same.

To begin to really raise awareness across the whole of Oman we created the campaign, Not Alone Oman. It was the first Mental Health Awareness Initiative of its kind in the Sultanate. The programme initially took the form of a video clip in both Arabic and English and introduced many disorders that could affect our mental state during our lifetime. Now the campaign has support from prominent public figures and personalities that add even more value and strength to the message, 'You are not alone in your suffering, we are with you'. We show real people who have struggled with their mental health, and how they have managed to deal with their struggles. We even have sponsored walks inside the shopping malls to get people to talk. Supporting mental health in the workplace should be fun, it should be something to get everyone talking and, when they are struggling, to make sure they don't feel alone.

THE BEST LAID PLANS ON PAPER RARELY WORK IN REAL LIFE

Ben Kay

FORMER ENGLAND RUGBY PLAYER | BROADCASTER AND PARTNER, PABLO LONDON | RUGBY EXPERT, BT | NON-EXECUTIVE DIRECTOR, LEICESTER TIGERS | COLUMNIST, THE TIMES | RUGBY ANALYST, ITV | DIRECTOR, BE LIFTED | TRUSTEE, RESTART

The big thing for me is to live in the moment, because everyone in sport has dips in form. It's that worry about what might happen; the fear of what's coming, the fear of the unknown. This often impacts performance, not one's own capability.

At certain points in my career, particularly early on, I'd get really nervous. Standing in the dressing room before we went out onto the pitch, there was a mix of terror and elation, but as soon as I was running around, I was fine. I worked out that I had to just enjoy it, and to almost welcome the fact that I didn't know what was going to happen. Now when things get on top of me, it's often because I'm worrying about what might happen. But as soon as I'm in the moment I can just take things as they come and adapt if I need to. I've now tried to give up worrying about what my future holds. Adaptability is key. No one should be told off for making a mistake, and I don't give myself a hard time, I learn from it instead. The best laid plans on paper rarely work in real life.

Fiorella Massey

FOUNDING CHAIR, FRIENDS OF MENTAL HEALTH FOUNDATION

A lot of research goes into the actual issue of mental health, but not much research goes into the solutions around mental health. I think prevention is so hugely important, because most mental health disorders start before the age of 24. If we can start providing support early on, we can reduce the prevalence of later problems. In every classroom, we're seeing increasingly young children exhibiting distressing symptoms of a gradual progression towards mental health issues, and we know that if those problems become entrenched, people can be left with lifelong challenges.

We have to start helping schools develop better programmes to assist with mental health issues when people are young, so that they can then make the transitions into either further education or apprenticeship schemes and the workplace. If a problem has already become entrenched, it will surface at some point, often in a traumatic way. I think a lot of businesses are struggling to report the wellness of their personnel, because the dialogue is not happening at an early enough stage for support to be provided in an integrated way. People are doing what they feel to be right in a very independent way, and of course some of these initiatives work, but unfortunately a lot of them are not trialled or tested.

To wait for a crisis to hit is not the way to create a better society. We need to listen, learn, collaborate and change.

To wait for a crisis to hit is not the way to create a better society. We need to listen, learn, collaborate and change.

Lord Mark Price (Mark Ian Price, Baron Price CVO)

FORMER MANAGING DIRECTOR, WAITROSE | DEPUTY CHAIRMAN, JOHN LEWIS PARTNERSHIP | FOUNDER, ENGAGING WORKS | CHAIRMAN OF FAIR TRADE UK | AUTHOR AND MEMBER OF HOUSE OF LORDS

Holly Price

BUSINESS DEVELOPMENT DIRECTOR, ENGAGING WORKS

Mark: As Theodore Roosevelt said, 'Nobody cares how much you know till you show how much you care'. Give people a sense of purpose so they care, reward them fairly, and give them the information to do their jobs well. They need to be satisfied and they need a good relationship with their line manager. I worked for the John Lewis Partnership for three decades and they do this well, their mission is the supreme happiness of their people. If their staff are happy, their customers will be happy and then they will make more money. So therefore, if people are happy it is better for the organisation and for society.

Holly: Engaging Works is an online platform that helps individuals have happier, healthier and more successful working lives. We do this by offering a range of services to help individuals find the perfect job, discover what company and industry is right for them, develop their career, communicate, connect and build a network, all in one place. Our free Workplace Happiness survey, comprised of 28 questions, helps individuals measure, track and improve their workplace happiness by giving them insightful data, development areas and action planning.

We also work with over 200 organisations to help them retain, recruit and communicate to improve workplace happiness and engagement. Research shows that organisations with a happy and engaged workforce have 20 per cent higher productivity, 20 per cent higher profit, lower wastage, lower sick absence, longer tenure and more. We (and our clients) not only recognise the commercial benefits of a happy and engaged workforce but also the altruistic benefits, helping build a happier society from the ground up.

Mark: We try not to get bogged down in the myriad of small things, but rather to celebrate every new customer. It's important not to get stressed out. If something is a bit late it is not a problem; the sun will implode in 4.5 billion years' time, and the earth won't be here. If it won't matter in five years, don't stress about it now.

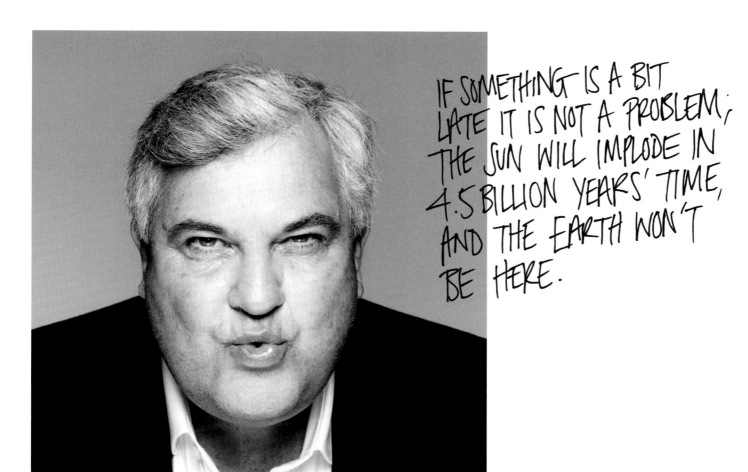

IF SOMETHING IS A BIT LATE IT IS NOT A PROBLEM; THE SUN WILL IMPLODE IN 4.5 BILLION YEARS' TIME, AND THE EARTH WON'T BE HERE.

Working with my daughter Jaz at Let's Reset, it's inspiring to see a business titan like Lord Mark Price work with his daughter and it's even better in meetings where Holly regularly takes the lead in the conversation. They seem very happy working together, but then happiness is at the core of their business.

Toks teaches at my gym in Berkhamsted. She is one of the toughest, most inspirational and challenging trainers that I have met. She is the NAC International Ms physique Muscle Goddess champion.

Toks Macaulay

ATHLETE AND FITNESS TRAINER

I used to be an investment banker in the city but when the recession hit I was made redundant. I was a Size 16 and needed to get fit. I didn't do any sport in school because, as an African, I was told by my family all that I should do was study. My ambition was to get into a size 12, so I hired Mark, a trainer who got me do basic stuff at first, like squatting and pull ups. I got fit, lost weight and enrolled in classes. I loved it and began to teach classes and fitness myself.

One day, across the gym I saw a bikini model called Becky Wright. I realised that I wanted to do that as well. I chatted to her and she immediately measured me up, right there in the gym with everyone watching, but, in a strange way, it spurred me on to do my first competition. I needed to understand my body, so I began to build muscle and take away all the fat through changing my diet.

Training enabled me to find out about my own strengths and focus on myself. I had never thought of that before. I had defined myself by being a mother, wife, businesswoman and a friend, not by who I am, what I am about and what I had to offer.

You can get inspiration from inside yourself and your own wellbeing. I don't think I look any different from a normal woman, but I know that I now give a lot of people inspiration. If I can change, if I can do it, anyone can.

You can control your energy by the way you breathe and use food as fuel so you feel better about yourself. If you feel amazing, then you get a magical feeling.

The mind is such a powerful tool, don't close it off. Think, 'I can. I will. It's possible'. Try not to say never or no. Instead just begin, take one step at a time and never quit. Finally, always be present and in the moment, enjoy the breathing and smile. This will affect how you are on the inside as well as the outside.

I questioned whether my first career made my soul sing.

Vanessa King

PSYCHOLOGIST | ACTION FOR HAPPINESS | LET'S RESET

When people have better wellbeing, they are more resilient and more likely to take care of themselves and subsequently live longer. Organisations who put wellbeing at their heart outperform and their share price is actually better. It was the first way of thinking that was evidence based. It's a win-win for employees, the organisations they work for and the wider community. Better wellbeing means they are more likely to contribute to their community and more likely to help others. The pace of change and new technologies emerging all the time make work stressful and people don't keep their stress at work. It bleeds out into their communities. We have to put wellbeing at the heart of organisations.

Without consciously knowing about wellbeing, before it was a thing, there were times when I had reached the edge of burnout and lack of meaning and I had to make some radical changes in my career from chartered accounting to psychology and wellbeing. I questioned whether my first career made my soul sing. I went on a personal journey and needed to do something that would make me feel better as a person. It was a bit of a journey to get to this point.

I was asked to write a book about wellbeing as a practical guide. I had never written a book before and I didn't know I was signing up to a crazy deadline. I had to go for it, but it meant I was working 14 hours a day for four months which took its toll. I discovered little tricks to help get me through like I would put my gym kit on in the morning and when I was stuck I would just go out for a little jog. It was the getting outside, getting a break and letting my subconscious brain take a break and work on its creative side which made the difference for me.

TOP TIP

Think about this as a shared responsibility from the top down. It's not just about individuals, but also the structure and culture of the business.

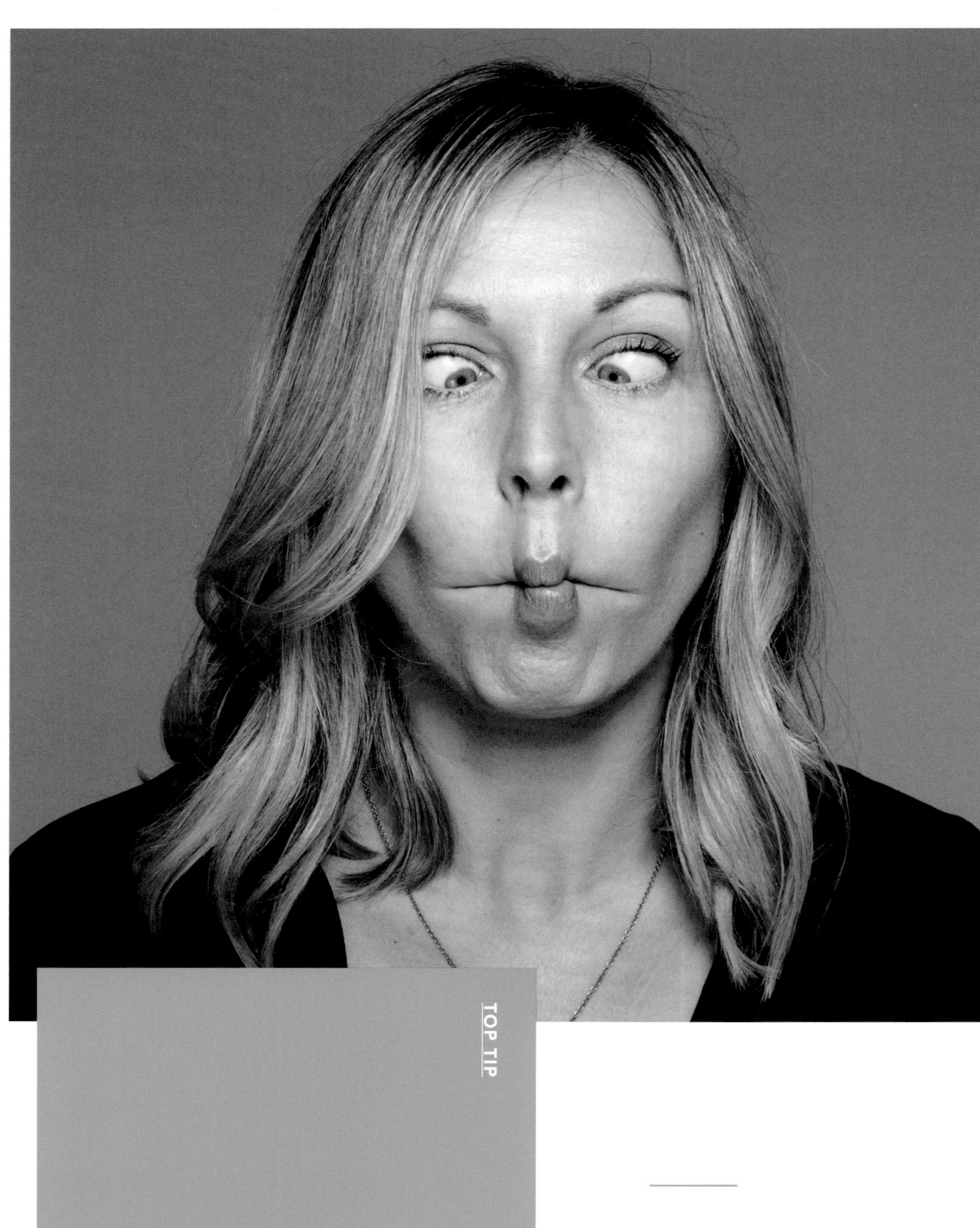

TOP TIP

Don't pigeonhole yourself and look after yourself from the inside out.

I love Jo Pratt's books, restaurant and cookery classes. Her writing is wonderful, her recipes are so clear and clever, and the end results, even when I cook them, are delicious. She is passionate about good, healthy food, which we all know makes us feel better. Two of my favourite books that she has written are In the Mood for Food and The Flexible Pescatarian.

Jo Pratt

CHEF, AUTHOR, RESTAURATEUR

Food is part of all of our lives because we all have to eat to survive and keep going. I love to help and inspire people to cook for themselves. We know that it gives people a sense of achievement and enjoyment, but it doesn't have to be from scratch and it should be fun. Amazing fresh ingredients can make your plate look inviting and your food look enticing. You can take a simple baked potato and fill it with a delicious and tasty, smoky, cheesy filling. Of course, you can opt for baked beans, but why would you do that?

Looking perfect is something that I constantly struggle with. Our food always need to look perfect in photo shoots, but that's not real life. So it's important not to get too worked up about perfection. At the end of the day, being served food cooked by someone else is always a lovely feeling and that's what really matters.

People just need to
– believe in
live in the

ek themselves
lves and
t.

Dale Naylor

PHYSIOTHERAPIST, SEVEN LONDON CLINICS | BIOMECHANIST | SPORTS PHYSIO | REHABILITATION

A batsman has 0.3 seconds to see a delivery. They take two sights of the ball spending the rest of the 0.3 seconds deciding a shot and playing it. Underperforming players take more looks, consider other options, second guess themselves and often check again. This is called noise and it leaves less time to deal with the delivery.

In life, negative speak, hesitation, and focusing on failure are types of noise. Once you make a plan it is better to happily back the plan and succeed (or not) rather than listen to noise, be miserable and succeed (or not). The difference is stress or anxiety and the result is the same (unless in some cases the noise negatively effects the outcome). I use strobes in practice to help eliminate negative thoughts in a game or remind players of themselves and their previous successes to block out the noise. Reduced visual input (two strobe flashes to catch a ball) forces players to back themselves without being able to see properly (reducing noise) from which flows confidence and leads to them trusting themselves. Try catching a ball in your left hand with your eyes closed, then try opening your eyes after it's thrown. Do it a few times then see how easy it is catching left handed normally afterwards. The feeling of ease is really you backing yourself.

Now think about how you perform when challenged, cut out the noise (thinking of other options, second guessing, checks, negative speak). Once you choose to do a thing, back yourself and make it happen. It's better and the outcome will often look after itself.

Angela Dixon

ACTOR AND CO-FOUNDER, EMPATHY EXCHANGE

I have worked as an actor and business coach for over 20 years. I have had the privilege of getting inside the worlds of others via the characters I have played and thousands of people from all levels of industry. What I notice is the overriding power empathy has to unlock our potential, develop great sustainable relationships and make us, and those around us, happier.

When I take on a role, I have to exercise unconditional positive regard for the character and unconditional love for myself in order to be authentic and engaging. I have to reserve my judgement, my values and beliefs, and really feel what it is like to be them, even if they repulse me. If I don't, the audience will sense that there is something not quite right and, in that moment, you've lost them. This process of deep understanding without prejudice, if applied in the 'real world', allows you and others to shine. It resolves conflict, unleashes creativity and precipitates authentic, honest conversations.

But how on earth do we do this? Think about your life at the moment. Who do you get on with? Who do you not? How valued do you feel at work? At home? With your friends? What are you doing that is making things work or not? All too often we are led by our chimp brain and emotional reflexes. We need to step out of the drama and consciously change our responses using empathy as the starting point. We need to relearn how to create environments for ourselves and others that bring out our 'a-game'. The skills are simple; the application takes effort.

My top tip for resilience and wellbeing is to build self-awareness and deep self-empathy. Understand what drives you, what upsets you and why. Once you have done that, do exactly the same for others, especially those who press your buttons, and let that knowledge change the way you behave.

for yourself
hen act on it.

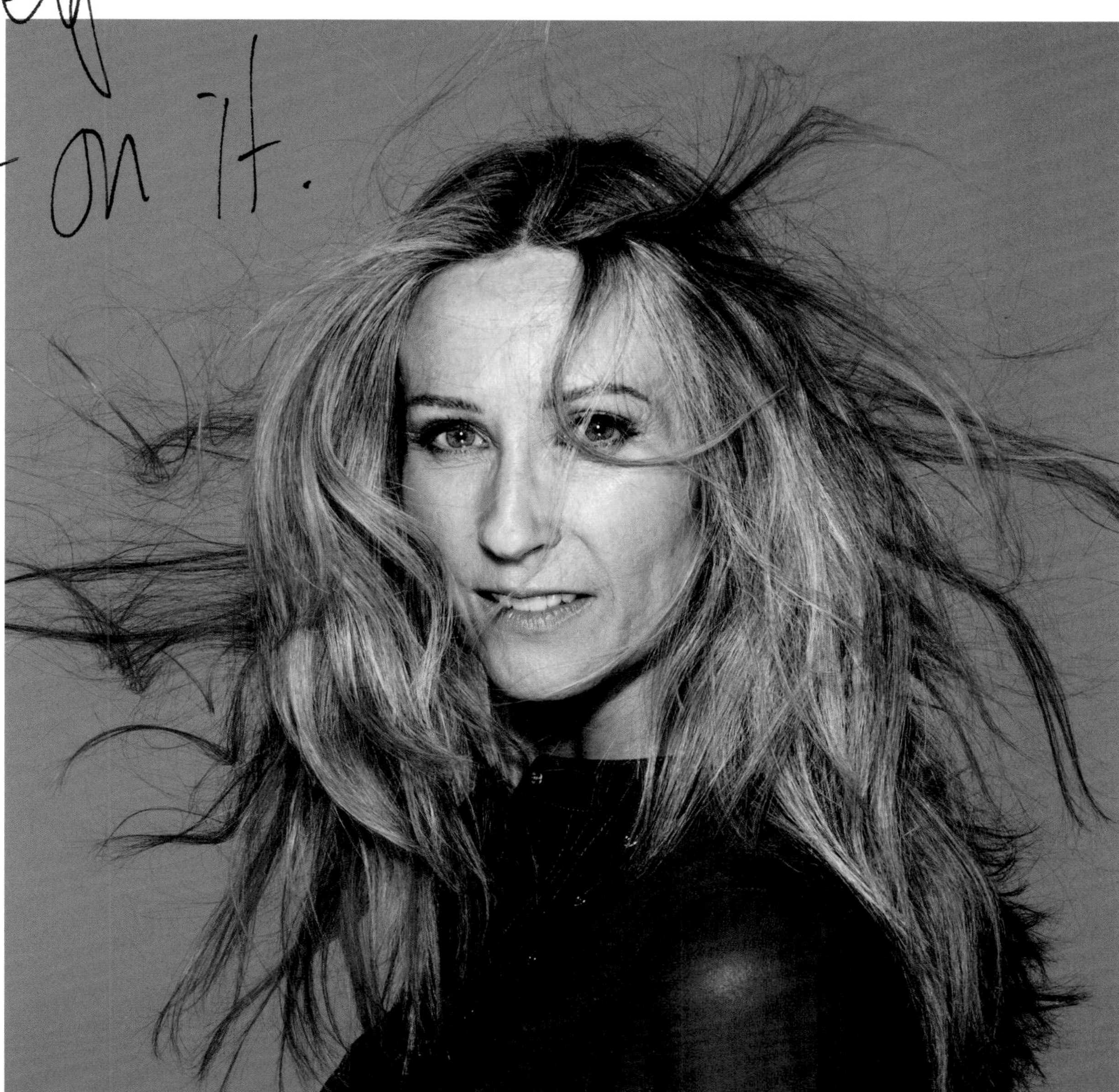

TOP TIP

Recognise that your success is determined by your people. They are the pulse of your peak performance and that pulse is driven by hearts. If businesses truly invested in the hearts of their people, they would flourish.

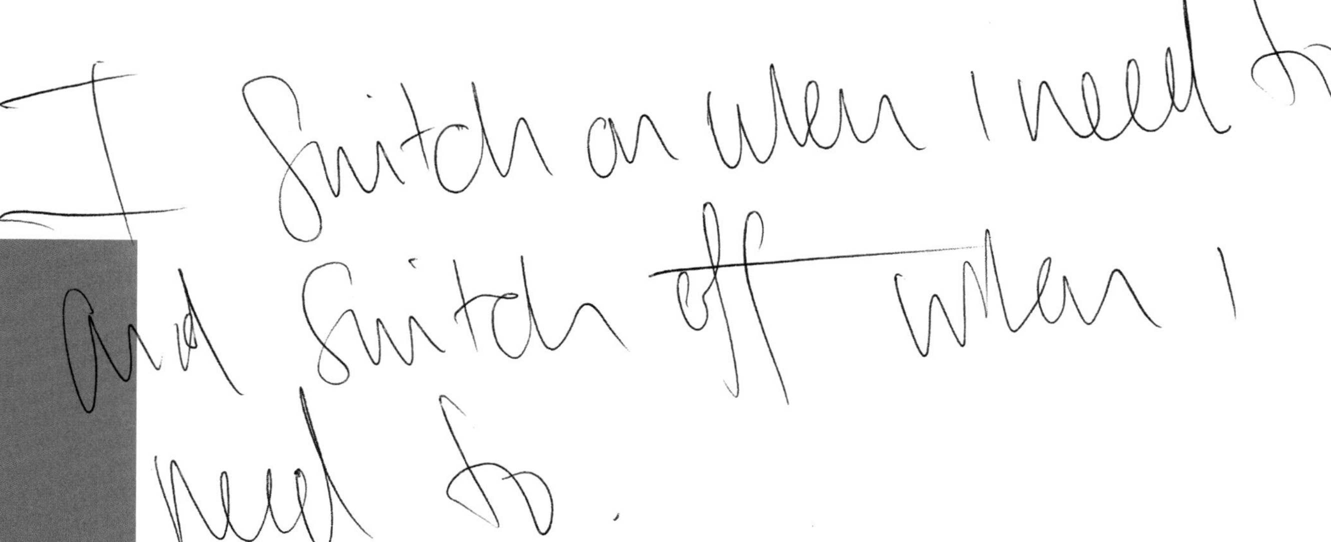
I Switch on when I need to
and Switch off when I
need to.

Dr Cat George

CLINICAL PSYCHOLOGIST, CAMDEN AND ISLINGTON NHS FOUNDATION TRUST

I work therapeutically with individuals who present me with complex mental health needs. In my work it is really important that I look after myself whilst I support others with their rehabilitation and recovery. Clinical supervision is a key component of this as it helps me to address any impact my work could have on me. I always take time to look inward and reflect on my practice to ensure that I am looking after myself and providing the best level of care to everyone I see. I always try to allow my brain some time to 'reset' itself as this helps me remain balanced.

I try to live by the words, 'Be kind to yourself', recognising that we are all just human and we all make mistakes sometimes. I believe we need to keep things as simple as possible by focusing on the everyday tasks which can make a positive impact on our wellbeing such as; a good night's sleep, eating well, going for a walk and doing more of what you love and enjoy. In our busy lives it can be very hard to find time for these areas as we all juggle so much.

When I find things are difficult I try to recognise them for what they are, take a break, and, as we say in the field, 'ground myself' in the present moment.

We all know the importance of keeping a good work-life balance. I switch on when I need to and switch off when I need to.

There are lots of myths about wellbeing in the workplace as little is really measured or analysed. It's important to know what makes a difference. The What Works Centre are looking at the evidence to show what has the biggest impact and Nancy is the Centre Director.

Nancy Hey

CENTRE DIRECTOR, WHAT WORKS CENTRE FOR WELLBEING

You are happiest in your life at 23 and at 68 and you are at your most miserable in your 40s. In your 40s you are most likely to be working hard. Your job is one of the top things that drives wellbeing and yet many people are miserable at work. Research suggests that the things that help people to flourish are packaged at work, such as achievement (which we get in spades), engagement or working at tasks with others, so why are we in this weird situation where we are not happy at work? This is the basis for our research at What Works Wellbeing.

A lot of organisations get that wellbeing is important and do ad hoc things to support their people, which is great, and some work. But we are trying to work out what makes a bigger difference. An organisation-wide strategy, job quality (good level of pay, having an interesting job and a good relationship with your line manager), work/life balance and flexibility are all important. Flexible working is popular, but we can see that working remotely can adversely impact others and it's more challenging for sectors such as teachers, construction workers, and musicians where, currently, everyone needs to be together at the same time. We overlay the psychological research to get positive connection, not just joy or happiness.

TOP TIP

Warm up and cool down.

We run from meeting to meeting and each carry emotional content that we drag from one activity to the next, and while we might do great prep for big set-piece activity, even the day-to-day matters. How do we change gear from relaxation or home to office and back? How do we move from our commute to a meeting, from high to low energy or from negative to positive emotion?

Louise Lumsden

HEAD OF FELLOWSHIP, ADVANCE HIGHER EDUCATION

I had to step up and support my children on my own after my husband left us. I am a Taurean. I am stoic and I like to be challenged, but this was a serious challenge and required resilience in spades.

I am determined and I want to be successful. I didn't want my personal circumstances to impede my career. My approach has always been that the past is in the past and we have to move forward to succeed.

I don't tell people everything about me because it is not always appropriate, but I am happy to share some things and that really helps me. I am the sort of person who wears their heart on their sleeve. Perhaps I am too honest, but that is how I exist and it is what helps me to cope and thrive. Making time and having opportunities to speak about things is so important.

THE PAST IS IN THE PAST AND WE HAVE TO MOVE FORWARD TO SUCCEED.

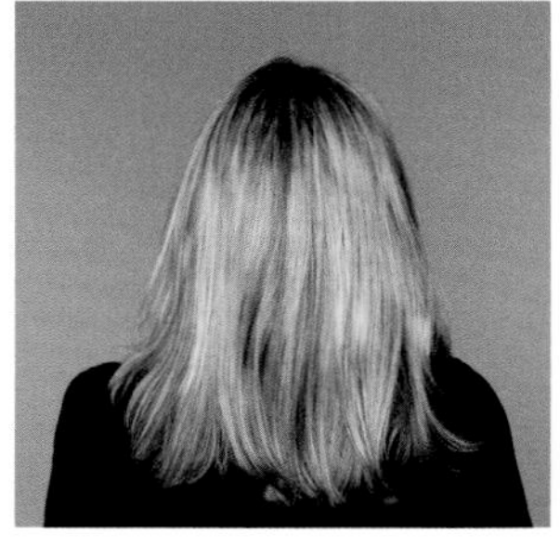

TOP TIP

Go out for a walk, get away from your desk, talk about anything and everything.

You don't need to be qualified to help, you just need to be kinder.

David Beeney

BREAKING THE SILENCE, FOUNDER

I got to 54 years old before I discovered self-compassion. I spent 36 years in the workplace battling anxiety and panic attacks every day and in silence. I thought it was weakness and no one would believe me. When I first outed myself about my mental health, I was concerned I would be treated differently and I was. People treated me better and they respected me more. This discovery now gives me permission to go through anxiety and panic attacks in front of people and I am as happy as I have ever been in my life.

My message to people is to share how you are really feeling, particularly guys. We think we have to be so tough and perfect and we can't cry. There is a phrase in sport which applies to the boardroom as well: 'Keep the dressing room with you.' It means you will take people with you if you inspire them. It is OK to be honest about what is happening in your home life. If you do, so will others and your team will be a better one as a result.

If you type 'physical health' into Google images you will see athletic people, but if you type in 'mental health' you will see people with their heads in their hands and in distress. Why is mental seen as negative yet physical as a positive? I have seven friends who have a personal trainer. I know this because they are proud of it. I wouldn't know if they had one for the mind because that is a counsellor and it is too embarrassing. What's more important: a healthy mind or getting rid of bingo wings?

Forget the statistics you hear, 1 in 1 of us will struggle with our mental health. If you aren't sleeping, that is poor mental health. If you feel anxious about something consistently, that is poor mental health. We have to make it easier in the workplace to be honest. Businesses have to set the tone from the top, those that do that will bring about a cultural shift. To me it is clear, forget about asking questions about work, ask people how their kids are. One day, when they bravely talk about a personal issue they will need to be signposted. You don't need to be qualified to help, you just need to be kinder.

Stacey Levine

CLINICAL PSYCHOLOGIST | INNATE HEALTH PRACTITIONER

I grew up the youngest in a family of three, and, from an early age, I became the peacemaker. Always listening, resolving conflict, keeping the balance. I somehow took on the belief that it was my responsibility to solve all of my family's issues. Later, that extended to my friends and peers, so it was no surprise to anyone when I decided to turn this amateur role into a professional one and graduated with a degree in clinical psychology.

The study of human beings is a fascinating topic and has always interested me. There are countless theories and models all aiming to understand why it is that people do the things they do and why they think the way they do. I have studied many of them, but it was the ideas of one enlightened man that made all the pieces fall into place. Sydney Banks uncovered why we do what we do and feel what we feel and that made complete sense to me and has been the inspiration of my work up until now.

He uncovered the heartbeat of all of our experiences – thought. Just as without a heart you would not be alive, without thought you could not have an experience of life. Literally all of our experiences are brought to life through the incredible power of thought. We are feeling what we think about moment to moment. When we truly see this, and the brilliance of the system, we begin to live more and more in an honest, free and authentic place.

Nelson Mandela saw this too and described it in his book, A Long Walk to Freedom, saying, 'As I walked out the door toward the gate that would lead to my freedom, I knew if I didn't leave my bitterness and hatred behind, I'd still be in prison'.

I am fascinated by the prisons that we lock ourselves into, often without even realising it. Thoughts we have about ourselves, others and the world. Chained by the memories, regrets and upset that we still carry in our head.

In this very moment, however, lies the potential and the capacity for insight; to see something more and unshackle oneself. But it begins with seeing that you are the keeper of that key to your cell. You are, as Syd said, one thought away from a whole new experience. You have that potential because you are that potential.

TOP TIP

The Joy of Missing Out (JOMO). This is the place where peace of mind, freedom, clarity, joy and love exist. This is what's left when the clutter of our minds is cleared.

TOP TIP

Music.

Music is my top tip for resilience and wellbeing in the workplace because the overwhelming neuroscientific evidence regarding music's effect on the brain demonstrates its power as a stress-busting and productivity tool.
We should all be fully harnessing its value in the workplace through well-curated playlists, music lessons, choirs, lunchtime gigs and music socials.

We are trying to get employers to help their employees listen to different music so they can be more productive.

Julia Jones

FOUNDER, FOUND IN MUSIC

I started in the world of wellbeing. 25 years ago, I worked as a sports psychologist and used music for anxiety control and as a way of helping athletes get through intense training. We have all been on the rollercoaster of ups and downs and I have used music extensively in very dark, black periods and also in the highs.

In business you need to put yourself in different situations, which can often be a struggle, and music can help with this. Open plan offices are not a good environment to get work done as there are too many distractions. People use headphones now to block out noise, but there is a lack of understanding as to what to listen to and how the choice of music can make a real difference to one's overall wellbeing. In fact, most people actually listen to the wrong music. We are trying to get employers to help their employees listen to different music so they can be more productive. Streaming has meant people are consuming more music now and there is a blurring between our home and work worlds. Why should the workplace be a different environment? Why should it be stiffer?

The world of sport is all about achieving peak performance – it is really precise. Just about all athletes use music because it is scientifically proven to help them achieve that. The same should therefore apply for the business environment. Why not emulate what has already been proven in the sports world?

Dr Fiona Mason

FORENSIC PSYCHIATRIST

Trauma in life can have a significant impact on future mental health, but I believe that what you learn from the past can positively inform your future. My destiny was shaped when I was a child and my mother went through a terrible illness which ultimately took her. That experience at a young age was etched on my psyche, and although I didn't know it, it drove my career.

As a psychiatrist I am a doctor that specialises in improving people's mental health, but I have also focused on workplace wellbeing to ensure that the needs of people at work are taken into account.

When people see me, they are often at their lowest point. You never know who will come through the door. You sometimes have to be their rock as they rely on you to be strong and help them through the darkest of days. I find I have to wear a mask as a clinician, as I have my own vulnerabilities. It's important to let my colleagues know the real me so they can support me – clinicians need support too.

I have learned to clearly communicate what I need and take responsibility for my behaviours and the choices I make. I have always had a choice, and, if I get a grip on my thinking, I can alter my behaviour. It gives me the freedom to do things differently – and it works the same way for my patients too.

In a work environment, and as a business leader, it is important to get to know who people really are beyond their job role – 'one size fits all' management just doesn't work when it comes to mental health.

Put simply, just understand and appreciate the real person and the value they add. In the workplace you want people to do their very best, and, as a leader, you need to find out what that is, and support them to do it. Culture in the workplace should not be underestimated. It is important to have board-level ownership, listen to the workforce and be informed by them. If the culture of the organisation avoids change, new initiatives often fail. Culture eats strategy for breakfast.

Culture
eats Strategy
for Breakfast.

TOP TIP

Do all you can to improve communication between people and listen to the quietest person in the room. They may not have the confidence to speak up but may have the most important thing to say. It's essential to really listen to what people are telling you so can respond effectively.

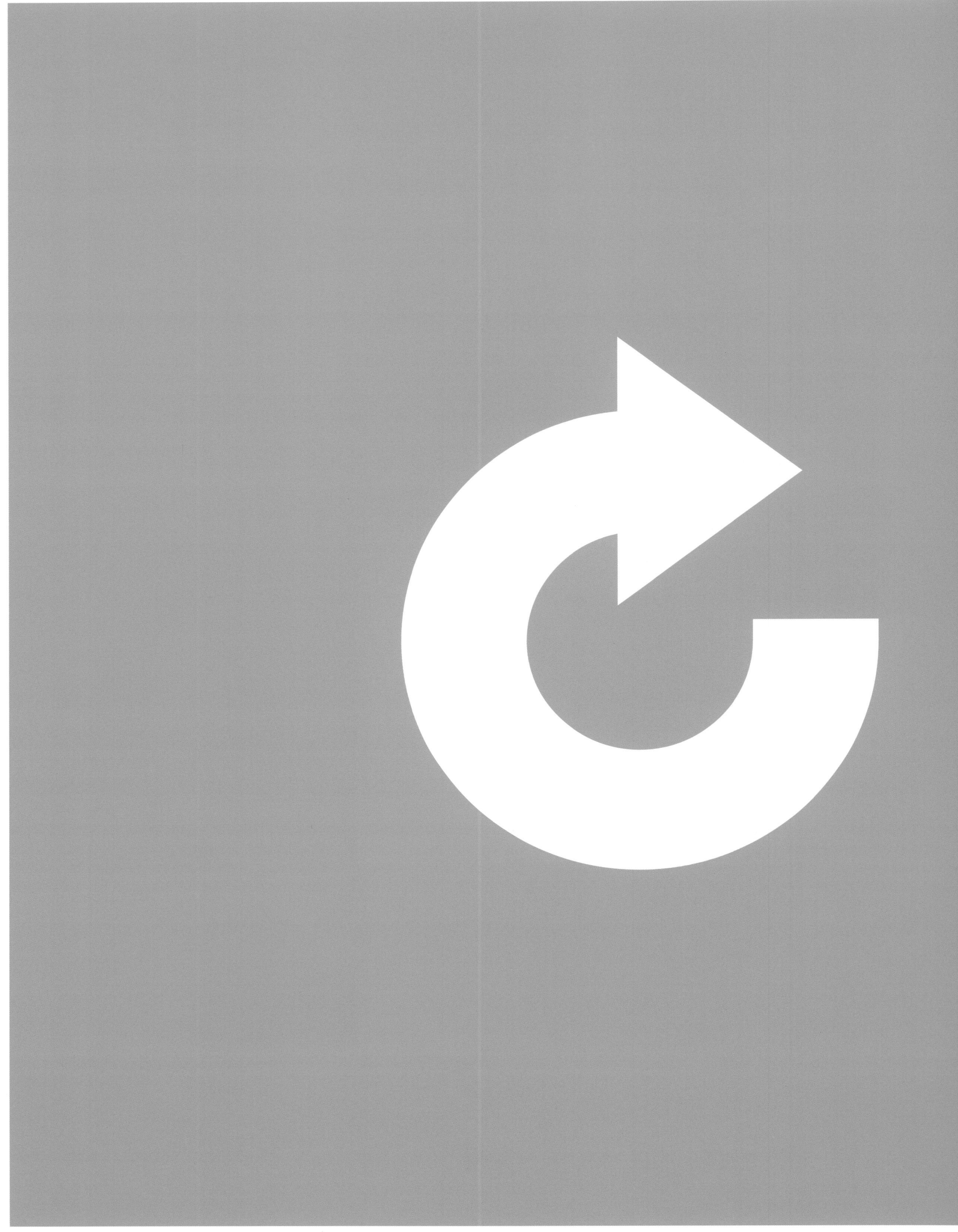

TOP TIPS

Reset yourself and your working environment to put wellbeing and resilience at the heart of your company and yourself.

<u>ONE</u>

Stay active. Do something physical as an active distraction from stress. It might be running, going to the gym, walking the dog, yoga, pilates, swimming or just breathing.

<u>TWO</u>

Try the theory of three lenses when facing a challenge in your personal or work life: look through the reverse lens: how is the other person thinking or feeling about the issue? Get perspective with the wide lens: who else is thinking about the problem and what is the lateral view? The long-term lens: how much will it matter in six months' time?

<u>THREE</u>

Sleep helps people repair themselves. Make sure you get enough of it.

<u>FOUR</u>

Practice gratitude. Be grateful for everything you have, as many others are worse off than you. Enjoy each day as it comes.

<u>FIVE</u>

Use music. Harness its value in the workplace through well-curated playlists, music lessons, choirs, lunchtime gigs and music socials.

<u>SIX</u>

Spend time outside and surround yourself with plants. Go for a walk, breathe in fresh air or work on the beach.

<u>SEVEN</u>

Laugh. When we laugh it feels brilliant.

Chapter five

The future generation

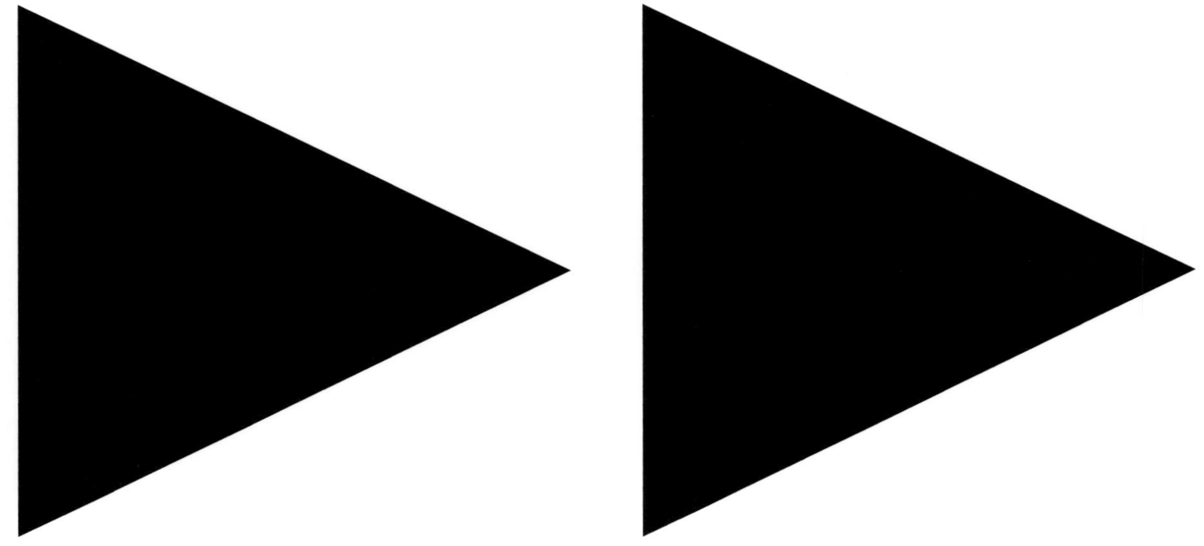

The future generation – FAST FORWARD

My daughter, Jaz, is studying Clinical Psychology at Exeter University and is founder of Let's Reset, Education. It was both Jaz and my son Sam's challenges and interest in mental health that led me to think differently about the workplace and ultimately create this book and business.

This final chapter begins to look at how Gen Z (children born around or after the year 2000) are thinking about the workplace and feeling the impact of an 'always on', digitally enabled world. It's a complicated place.

According to the NHS, 16.9 per cent of 17 to 19-year-olds in the UK suffer from a mental health disorder, and evidence suggests that these problems are exacerbated when starting university, work and apprenticeships. Research by The Economist also notes that they are less hedonistic, better behaved and lonelier than ever before.

Also, worryingly, in 2017 in the UK, there were 95 recorded student suicides and the number is rising.

This generation is having to learn to navigate a new and stressful social landscape. Alongside the ordinary stresses of becoming an adult, millennials and Gen Z are exposed to an environment of constant connection and instant gratification though social media. It can often be hard to keep up.

I believe that in making the transition from childhood to adulthood, it's important that young people have strong support systems to help their wellbeing and teach resilience. This includes not only friends and family, but employers, educational environments and colleagues as well.

Gen Z is a part of a connected world (unlike millennials, many of whom can still remember dial-up internet access). They are hypermobile multitaskers, used to navigating status updates through a dozen or more apps at once. They switch between tasks quickly or focus deeply on one task for long periods.

The benefit of this upbringing is that we can provide them with many different responsibilities in the workplace to keep them happily engaged. Unlike many of my contemporaries, who started a working life wanting to make money and be promoted, Gen Z, like millennials, are keen to immediately do good at the same time as creating value.

Young minds can be a business's greatest assets and they are our future leaders. It's crucial that we reset how businesses function to provide young people with the support they need to ensure their optimal wellbeing and performance, so they can help commerce to thrive.

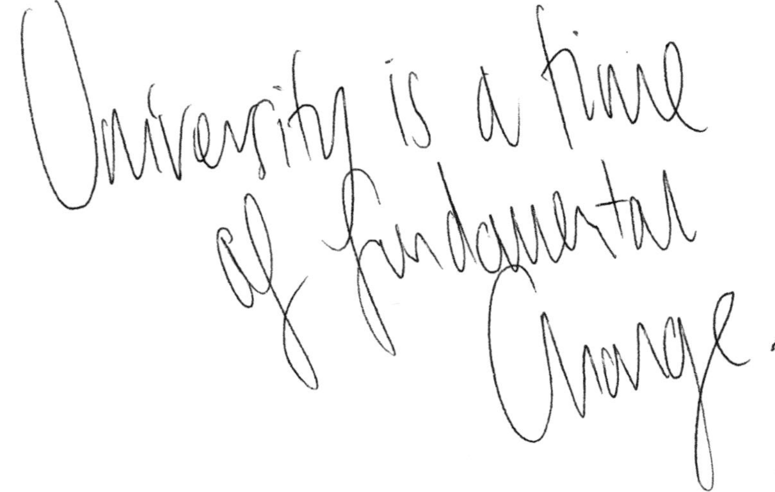
University is a time of fundamental change.

Jaz Thompson

MASTERS IN CLINICAL PSYCHOLOGY, EXETER UNIVERSITY | FOUNDER OF LET'S RESET EDUCATION

University is a time of fundamental change. For many it is the first time living away from home and navigating various social and academic pressures. It is therefore no surprise that for some people, their mental health can deteriorate.

For me, my first year was a whirlwind. The combination of constantly meeting new people and studying a new subject that I loved was exciting, and the year went by in a flash. However, my second year was much more challenging. The blur of first year was a distant memory, and university was no longer new and exciting; it was just the norm. I hadn't taken a breath in my first year to work out how I was coping with the new lifestyle. This in turn led to me to start feeling lost, and a black cloud was slowly but powerfully starting to form in my head.

I was diagnosed with depression in early December and started seeing various counsellors to work out why I was feeling like this. Truthfully, at the time I had no idea why I was feeling low. My family was healthy, my studies were going well and I loved Exeter University, so in my head it didn't make sense why I didn't feel happy, which in turn made me feel even worse.

At the time I was living with four girls and I decided to tell them what I was going through. Although the majority of them were very supportive, one of the girls told me they, 'Didn't believe in depression', which really struck a chord with me. I was baffled that someone who was so well educated could think something so fundamentally untrue and gradually I realised that others felt the same. I decided not to react negatively to the comment and created an Instagram account in order to educate people about mental health and support young people struggling. Without knowing it, that Instagram account (@wellbeing_in_mind), became my own therapy, and although I intended to use it for helping other people, I was helping myself as well.

I was lucky enough to find an amazing counsellor who I saw or spoke to every week. The lessons she taught me are still invaluable. The main one is the importance of self-care and learning, that doing things for yourself is not selfish, it is essential. This whole experience and the things I have learnt these past couple of years has made me want to make a difference in universities. To help put wellbeing and resilience to the forefront of university life, not just when students are in a crisis.

I received excellent help through my university's wellbeing services, but it was almost too late. I had to go onto antidepressants and get counselling, but I believe that if I had the self-care tools that I have now, I would not have had to go through most of that. It is just as important to prevent mental illness through positive wellbeing and resilience teaching as it is treating mental illness itself.

TOP TIP
Take time out for yourself.
Self-care is never selfish.

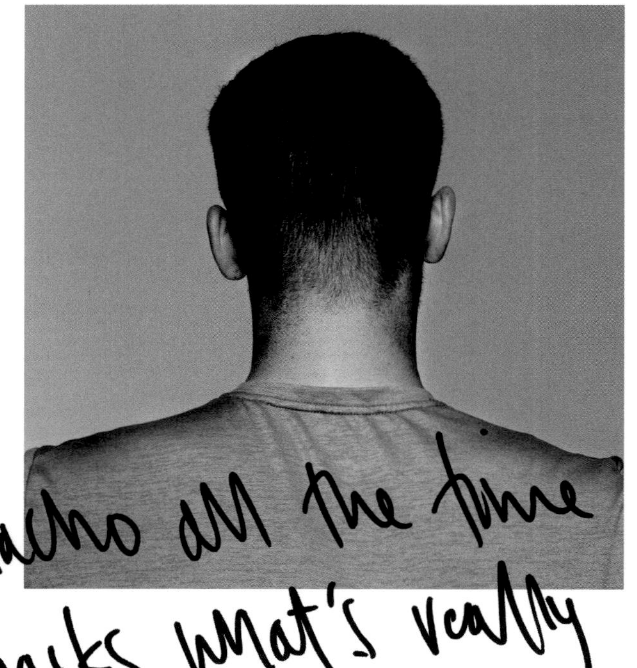

Being macho all the time just masks what's really going on underneath.

Julian Cash

PROFESSIONAL TENNIS PLAYER

I have just come back from surgery and it has been up and down, not knowing whether I will be able to get back on a tennis court. The hardest thing is the daily grind of rehab. I started to see a psychologist, unfortunately too late, but they did introduce me to new techniques which have really helped me to build my resilience and aid my recovery.

Meditation and yoga have done the most to help me to get back on track. After my surgery, my heart rate went up due to the high levels of stress and anxiety I was experiencing, but the meditation and yoga have helped to bring it down. I cannot believe how much the impact of the surgery affected my whole life and my fears of perhaps not being able to do what I love again. I feel so much happier now and back to the way I was when I was competing. I am now back focused on my goals. I travel a lot in my job and I get to see a variety of cultures and people from all walks of life. I see real people and it makes me appreciate how lucky I am. I am looking forward to getting back to that grounded way of thinking.

I have learned to listen to the people around me. Listening to others who know more, or know you well, helps to give a better perspective. I would always encourage others to not be afraid of seeking help. It is easy in today's society to ignore that. I went into a deep low straight after the surgery, but it was my friends who noticed I wasn't the same person and came to support me.

In sport, you are built up the whole time to be strong and I am not always sure it is the best way to go about it. Being macho all the time just masks what's really going on underneath. It is better to address them, look them in the eye and deal with them, not hide them away.

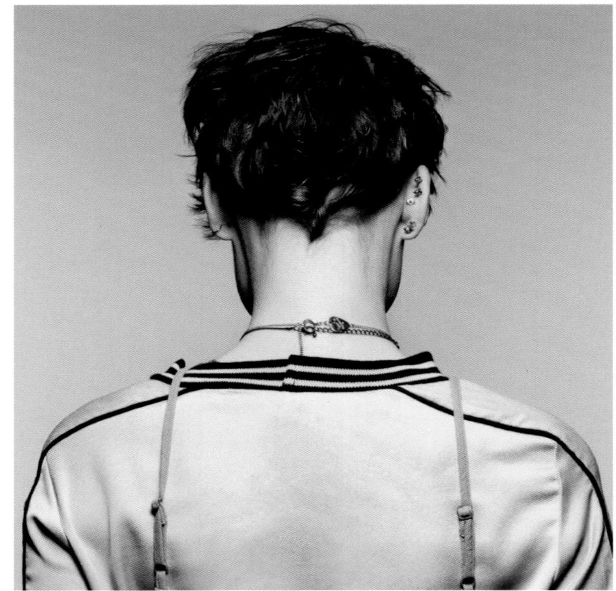

TOP TIP

Don't let any struggle define you. If you need a break, take it. If you can't handle something, ask for help. Looking after yourself isn't a weakness. It'll make you a better, more efficient and happy person in every way if you pay attention to your own needs as much as everyone else's.

What I have learned is that the most important thing is to know yourself and to do things to help yourself

Teddy Foley

APPRENTICE FLORIST

I identify with some labels but they don't define me. I am non-binary and queer. My mental health was a huge obstacle when I was in mainstream schooling – I struggled to put structure in my life and organise myself. It became a huge problem and I dropped out of school. Time and experience have helped me to deal with it all. There is no quick and easy way out and I have come to the point where I just accept that I need to learn from it and understand what works well for me. I became aware that some things upset me more than others and I now try and find ways to manage them. I have an amazing group of friends who are really supportive. They are open and we have been able to talk about things. My family are amazingly supportive, and they let me take the reins to help me steer my way through things.

Mental health is completely different for different people. What I have learned is that the most important thing is to know yourself and to try things to help yourself. Some things will work and some won't, but it is better to have tried and failed than not to have tried at all.

Cam Bleakley

STUDENT

Throughout my adolescent and adult life, I have had ups and downs concerning my mental health. A combination of various scenarios has influenced the way I feel. A difficult relationship early on helped me to build up resilience without realising it at the time and I became stronger mentally. Quickly I became aware that you can only better yourself if you yourself want to.

My secondary school breached my trust with sensitive information and, as a result of this, I lost faith in the mental health care processes in education. Thankfully, at university, it was a completely different story. Mental health is a priority and a number of events are held throughout the year to encourage discussion and self-help. For example, puppies are brought in for students to meet and play with. Information about who to talk to about your mental health is fed subtly and is not over-distributed so you see the messages just the right amount. This is a good method as it allows any individual to have the space they need, always knowing there is someone there if needs be.

If I could recommend one thing to better your mental health, it would be to spend time outside and surround yourself with plants. Caring for plants gives you a purpose, they wouldn't be alive without you watering them, so a sense of natural satisfaction is induced.

My one tip for businesses giving support in mental health and wellbeing is to choose a method of communication to give out information on a regular basis. Information about help should be there, but not 'in your face' as you don't want to create pressure inside the mind of an individual who is seeking help. It needs to be approached in a holistic way, not a corporate routine.

TOP TIP
Spend time outside with nature.

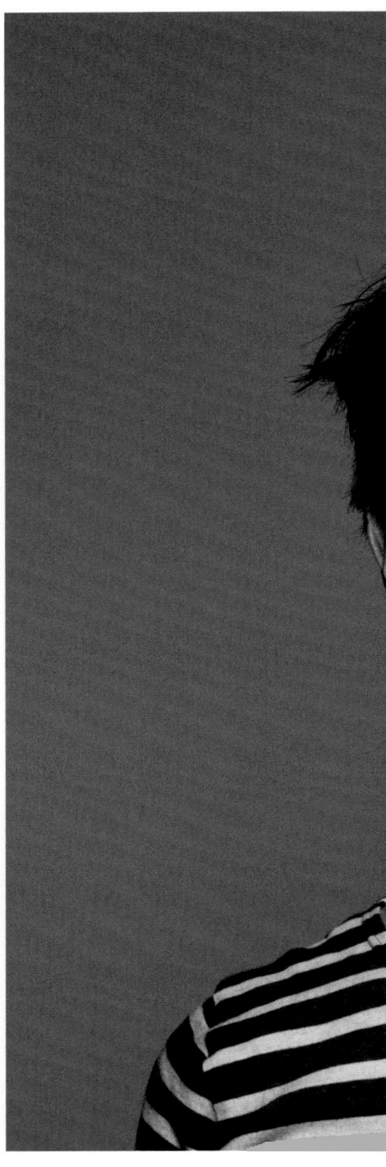

I REMEMBER CONSTANTLY REPEATING
THE PHASE IN MY HEAD 'THIS TOO SHALL PASS'

Will Pope

PHOTOGRAPHER | FILMMAKER

At 16 I was diagnosed with heart disease. It was at a very late stage and they thought I wasn't going to survive. I had eight open heart surgeries and was eventually given a heart transplant. However, the recovery after the surgery wasn't easy at all.

You can panic and think, 'Oh God this is a terrible thing that's happened to me', or you can take a positive perspective and focus on getting through it. I remember constantly repeating the phrase in my head, 'This too shall pass'.

Clinically there were professionals helping me, giving me medication for my mental health, which really helped, but it wasn't until I left hospital that my recovery really started. Once I was at home, I could walk up and down the stairs, eat my Mum's cooking and play with my dog. What really kept me going though was thinking about what the future held for me and what I was going to do with my life once I had recovered.

I used to have a lot of anxiety. When I went to bed, I'd become very anxious about my career or friends or anything really. And I think I've got past that through practising acceptance.
I remember speaking to a fellow struggling artist and talking about the issues we both have, and we agreed that we are so privileged to have these issues, as opposed to many people in the world who suffer from far worse. Trying to take a positive perspective on my problems is really important for me.

TOP TIP

To always be grateful. My organ donor allowed me to live. Without his selfless decision, I wouldn't be alive today, so being grateful is something I think about every day.

A happy workplace is a pretty productive one and that is the same with sport.

Tom Lace

CRICKETER, MIDDLESEX

Particularly in sport, wellbeing support is only there if you want it to be and if you actively make yourself available to it. It is still a taboo topic and I think people are still scared to talk about it, or even embarrassed. In the last couple of years, it is something I have prioritised a lot as I think it is something that is fundamentally important, in order to play well and remain happy. As much as you don't want it to be, playing cricket becomes a lifestyle, especially over summer, moving here, there and everywhere, so if you are not feeling your best emotionally on the pitch it can transfer physically in performance.

To help improve my wellbeing I have had to find something outside of cricket to invest time in. There are other sports I like to play and watch in order to relax, but I am still trying to find a hobby completely unrelated to sport in order to properly unwind. I love music but I am still young and have time to play around with lots of things and find a hobby I really love. It is important to me that I am comfortable outside my work environment, because demons can start to creep in when work begins to take over your life.

Cricket can be a lonely place if you don't look after yourself, but this is not an alien feeling. When I first started playing, I was embarrassed to talk about these negative feelings but once I started to open up, I realised lots of people were in the same boat and feeling the same things. When you realise it's not an unnatural feeling it becomes a lot easier to deal with and manage.

TOP TIP

Celebrate the success of your colleagues and friends as much as you can. It takes the focus off your own performance and happiness is contagious.

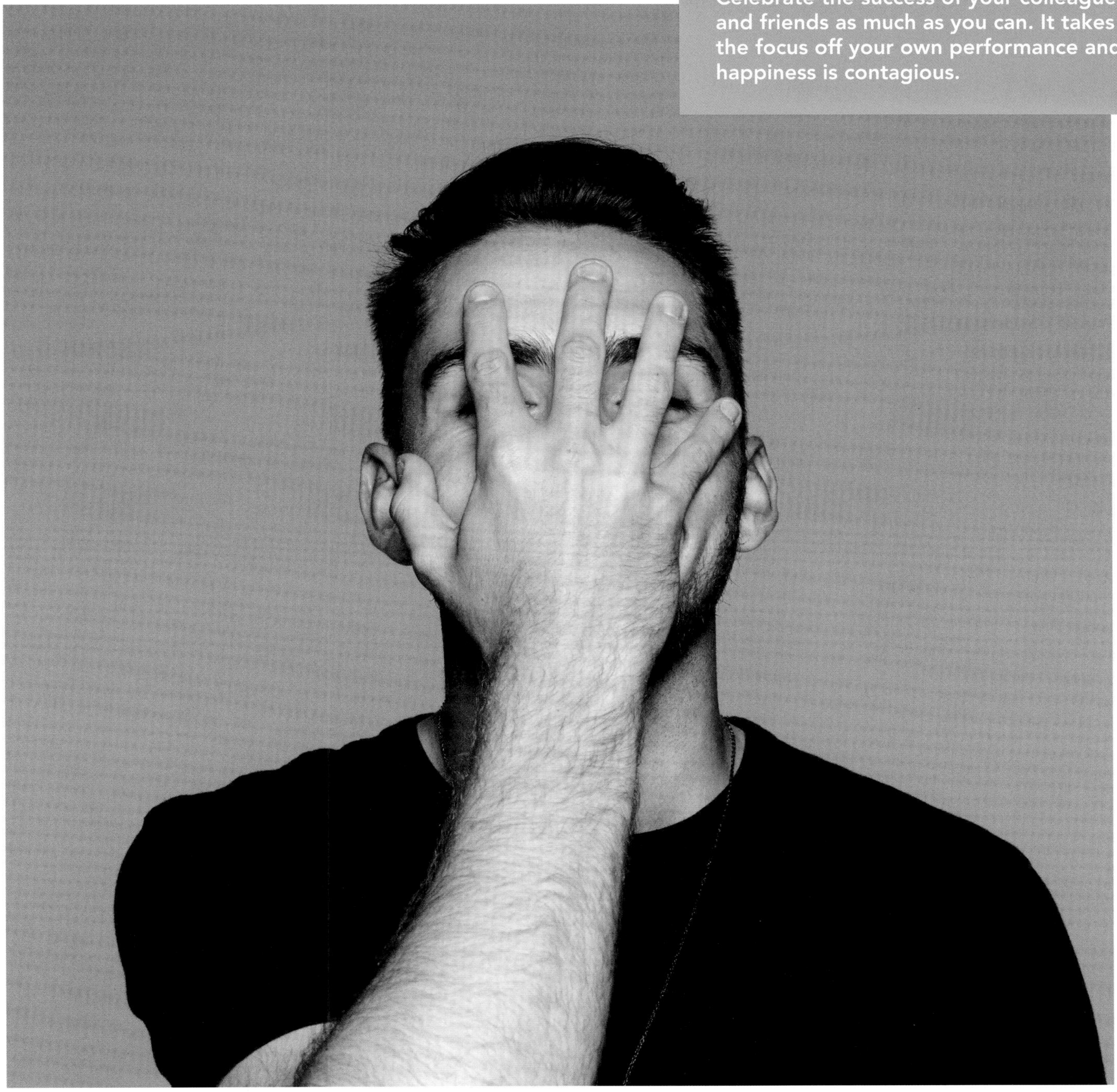

Zahra Hulf

PSYCHOLOGY GRADUATE, UNIVERSITY OF EXETER

A lot of people think university will be a breeze, the best three years of their lives even. But for a lot of people it can be the most challenging three years they've experienced thus far. This was the case for me. I went from living at home, in a very contained and protected environment, to living away from home and having to work it all out for myself. There were a lot of influences at university, some good and some really not so good, and at times I felt totally lost and unsure of my direction or purpose.

What made it worse was seeing everyone else having such an incredible time. The pictures that I'd scroll through every day on Instagram or Facebook would highlight to me just how much of an amazing time everyone else was having. So naturally I felt I had to put a mask on to act as if I too was having the time of my life. But the more I pretended, the more lost I felt. I surrounded myself with people who weren't right for me, because I wasn't being honest about who I was. Externally, I appeared like I was outgoing and always happy. Internally I felt totally isolated.

When I finally reached my breaking point, one of my best friends said to me, 'I would have had no idea you were ever feeling this bad. You always look like the happiest person in the room'. I think it just goes to show that no matter what you see on social media or what face anyone puts on, you really have no idea what's going on inside.

Suffering alone was the mistake I made. If I had spoken to my friends about the way I was feeling earlier and stopped trying to hide how I really felt, I would've realised that the majority of people were feeling the exact same way. I would've realised that what I was seeing on social media wasn't accurate at all and I would've been able to get support.

TOP TIP

Be kind to yourself. The most important thing I have learnt is to be my own number one fan. Someone once told me that rice plants grow faster and more healthily if you say kind words to them every day. Whether this dubious fact has any science behind it or not, I have found that, since treating myself with the same love and compassion I give to others, I have begun to flourish and bloom just like a rice plant.

Sam Thompson

STUDENT

I am eccentric. There are two me's; there is the Sam with lots of energy, and the introspective, quieter Sam. Sometimes I have to force myself into the other Sam. It can be draining and I can feel hollow inside as a result. I have had periods where I have had a lot of bad mood swings and I try and keep myself to myself when that happens. For about a year I went through a bad period of depression and now I don't show people my vulnerability, which helps me get through it. If others feel like this, I would suggest they find what makes them happy – a small happiness is better than nothing. Just take little steps like a meal or a shower. I find it helps and it enables me to stop feeling sorry for myself.

Happy Sam is more pleasant to be around. When I am with people, I can see that we match each other's energy so I try to be upbeat and they will follow suit – it is contagious.

As a high functioning autistic person, it is sometimes hard to process that I will never fully understand that connection with others. The benefit is that I think differently. I see ideas, patterns and have thoughts that most people don't. I also have a massive ability to retain facts, so my friends love me being on their quiz team.

I don't want to go to university, but I do want to be challenged and continue to learn. I'm smart and I want to work hard but need to be in a culture that likes to support and empower people who think differently, not just sit at a desk doing the same job every day from 9-to-5.

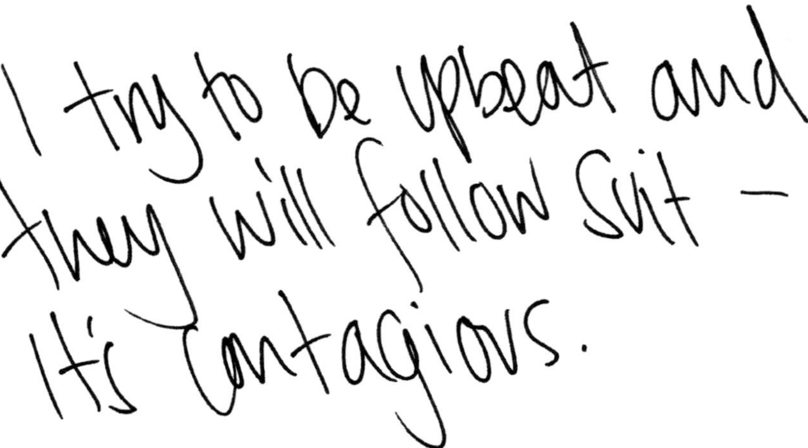
I try to be upbeat and
they will follow suit –
It's contagious.

TOP TIP

Just try and stay calm and carry on.

TOP TIPS

These are the leaders of our future workplace; let's listen to what they want and need.

ONE
I'd like to have a safe space in work where it is OK to take a bit of time out for yourself. It might be a physical space to go to or just the unspoken acceptance that it is OK to have a break.

TWO
I want to be inspired, challenged and supported to be my very best self.

THREE
An employer should be someone who has an interest and understanding in my life outside of work, allowing a connection that is not simply business focused but one based on a personal connection.

FOUR
I'd like to receive information and training on a regular basis to help increase my resilience and wellbeing but it needs to be approached in a holistic way, not just as part of corporate routine.

FIVE
I'd like to work in a culture of acceptance and understanding at work, so we all feel safe and supported.

SIX
In our careers, skill is nurtured over a long period of time. We should place the same emphasis on our wellbeing as we do on our performance so it isn't left behind.

SEVEN
We should work in a flexible environment where we are measured on our contribution, support and proactivity, rather than how many hours a day we spend in the office. We should also recognise that some people need longer breaks than others.

Huge thanks

This is the second book that Rankin and I have worked on together and it has been a labour of love for so many people. I have loved learning and hearing the stories of the people in this book and others who couldn't be included here. So to everyone who has put up with me on this brilliant journey of discovery and particularly those below, thanks.

It has been such a privilege to create this book with my fabulous friend, Rankin, a photographic genius who saw into the hearts of the individuals and captured their other self. Thank you to his amazing team including Christine Wright, Christine Jones and Flora Rogers for all their advice, help and support; Ellen Stone for her keen eye and publishing expertise; Beverley Luckings for brilliant PR ideas and intros; Nick and Marco Antonio, the amazing 'Glam Team', for making everyone feel relaxed and looking real and CEO of RANKIN, Richard Pinder, for corralling everyone together. And it's not over – the campaign from the essence of this book is being developed and will appear in early 2020.

To everyone who has told their stories in the book and on our community platform **letsreset.com**, you have given up your time, but, more importantly, you have opened your hearts and minds to tell your story, provide insight and expertise and help us reimagine the workplace with wellbeing and resilience at its heart. A special mention to Zahra Hulf and Claudia Collingbourne for their unbelievable dedication and huge amount of hard work in pulling this book together.

With Helen Gorman, Katie Reddin-Clancy and Angela Dixon, your interviewing, chasing, cajoling and harassing of people, partners and friends to bring all the stories together, has been amazing.

Massive thanks to Vitality who have been our brilliant partner in this book. Particularly Greg Levine, who shared this vision with me; Neville Koopowitz and Deepak Jobanputra who feature in the book, plus Robyn Winfield and Keith Kropman for their support.

On design, huge thanks to Johnny Hornby, Sarah Golding, Deborah Kerr, Andy Bumpus, Matt Hunt, Tom Atkinson, Nathan Harper, Kate Scally and Sam Walsh at Pulse Creative London (The&Partnership and News UK) for designing and editing Let's Reset; your proficiency and amazing talent has been awesome. Thanks also to David Dinsmore and News UK for taking on the conversation. Thanks to David Arkell at Pureprint and &Printed for printing Let's Reset.

Thanks to many of my friends who have supported the promotion of the book, including Annette King, Erris de Stacpoole and Lizzie Dewhurst at Publicis Groupe for their fabulous PR support and event organisation. To John Lewis Partnership for our fabulous launch at the The Place, Westfield. Thanks to Richard Kilgarriff and his Bookomi team who were responsible for our special breakfast at Annabel's. Sarah Harbon and Lou Bennett at Benefit Cosmetics who are empowering women every day and are our glamorous partners on a short film series of some of the people in the book. Russ Kane who has created the Let's Reset programme on his Men and Women's Wellbeing Radio stations. Also, thanks to William Eccleshare and the team at Clear Channel, Richard Bon and Joanne Henderson, for promoting the campaign on their sites in 2020.

Thanks to my friends and colleagues at Advertising Week, Whispers of Serenity, CPFC, Hearts and Minds, Oystercatchers, Xeim/Centaur, Facebook, WPP, Brainlabs, Google and the new Let's Reset team for helping me make this idea a reality – many who are now working with us on Let's Reset programmes. Thanks also to Charles Thiede, Jon Beer and the team at Zapnito for building our brilliant platform.

Thanks to Stevie Spring, Chairman of Mind, for her encouragement. A donation from the profits of this book and business will go to Mind.

To my best girlfriends Fiona Read, Liz Penny, Sonya Orlov, Liz Moseley, Jill McDonald, Leah Holroyd and Tammy Manning. They all make me laugh and, with their wider families, they are always there for me.

And, last but not least, a big thanks and love to my family for putting up with me while I began my new obsession. To Jaz, whose idea to support wellbeing was the start of this book. To Sam, who has shown me how to live life with a different perspective and to Feilim, who is my guiding light and impetus to launch Let's Reset. To my Mum, who is the reason that Rankin and I started on this journey together. Thanks also to my Dad, David, Tam, Guy, Susie, Veryan and the Minchin bunch who have given me so much love, inspiration and content for this book.

Thanks, finally to Janet Heath. We all miss John so much, but I am an entrepreneur and a surfer because of him, and this book is a culmination of so much that he taught me.

Thank you all… and breathe.

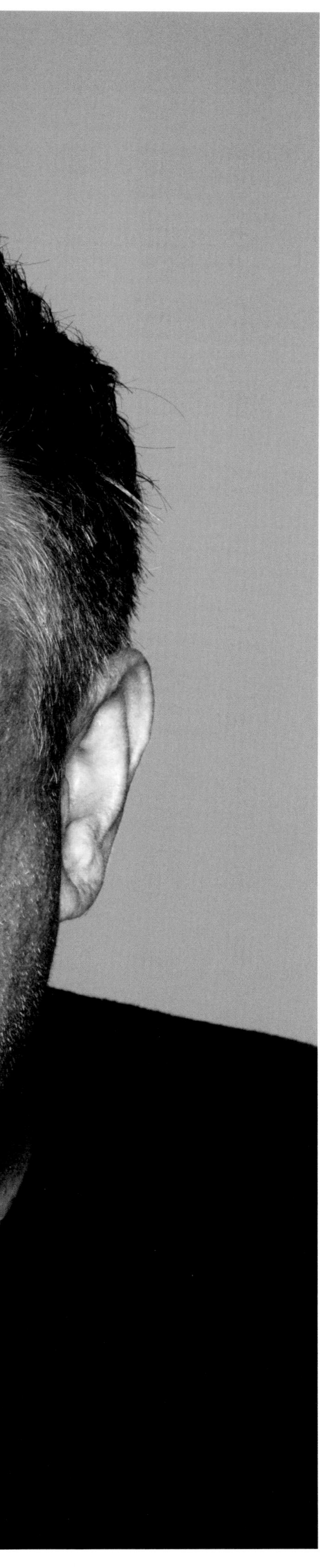

let's reset

RANKIN

Vitality

The & Partnership

News UK

PULSE CREATIVE

Clear Channel

bookomi.

PureprintGroup

&Printed

Public Offerings Ltd.

WPP

benefit SAN FRANCISCO

facebook

OYSTERCATCHERS

CENTAUR

Annabel's

All efforts have been made to truly reflect the interviews held with the people featured in this book. Some of the contributors may have changed role since their portraits were taken.

A CIP record of the book is available from the British Library.

First printed October 2019
Published by Rankin Publishing Ltd.

ISBN: 978 - 0-9955741-3-7